PRESCRIPTION

Isidore Rosen

REPEAT PRESCRIPTION

Dr. Isidore W. Crown

Keter Classics

London, England.

Keter Classics
37 Reid House
Bampton Road
London SE23 2BJ

First published 1996
© Dr Isidore W. Crown 1996
Set in Baskerville
Typesetting by MKG Typesetting, Bridgwater, Somerset
Print production by LPL Print Service,
Bridgwater, Somerset

A catalogue record for this book is
available from the British Library.

ISBN 0-9525373-0-3

CONTENTS

1

Confidence Tricksters

I commenced in my own practice in January 1953, but realised from the first day that I was going to have a struggle in making a living from my National Health patients – Dr Morgan my predecessor had only bequeathed me 200. It has always been impossible for a single-handed doctor with just a few hundred patients and with a young growing family to support to rely just on the National Health Service for a living. To supplement my income in 1953, I worked some nights as a locum for a ten-doctor rota in the East End and when on duty for a particular doctor I slept on his surgery premises.

One of the doctors in this rota had a surgery in New Road, off the Commercial Road, and this chap's housekeeper was a real, shrewd, old lady, who never missed a trick. Her existence was known to every sailor in the West India Docks nearby, for it was not unusual for a foreign-speaking sailor to turn up in the early hours of the morning and complain of pain and discharge when pissing.

The story was always the same: one of the 'local ladies' had propositioned him, the price was right, he had accepted her offer and had sex with her. A few days after the experience he wished he had had more curb on his desires, he suffered agonising pain every time he wished to urinate and one of his friends had directed him to this doctor's surgery.

My sleep was of little importance to this housekeeper when one of these chaps turned up, she always woke me up and insisted that I give him a penicillin injection. She gave me two pounds in cash for the jab, an enormous sum of money for me in the fifties, but what she had actually charged the poor chap I never found out. I never dared to ask. She was a right old madam. I was scared of her and her acid tongue. She had such a dominating personality! A bad word about me to the doctor who was running the rota and I would have been out of a job! I needed the money, even though it was only two pounds for a night's work for the ten doctors. Her employer's share would have been two shillings (ten pence), but from the way she made me work I am certain that she had not heard slavery had been abolished in the nineteenth century. The fact that I am Jewish, her boss was Jewish, and she was too, made no difference. Her main aim in life appeared to be to make sure her employer got full value for employing me.

Whilst working for this rota in 1954, I was called to a house in the East India Dock Road, in the early hours of one morning, to be confronted by a bevy of scantily-dressed young ladies who were obviously the source of the supply of young sailors to the New Road surgery. There was however one exception amongst these *beauties*. It was the lady in charge, a middle-aged lady, fully dressed, who asked me to examine a young girl who was screaming with pain, lying on a couch in the dining room.

The girl was about eight years old and I had the devil's own job trying to examine her. When I finally managed to do so, with the help of three girls who held the struggling mass down, I found that she was suffering from acute bilateral otitis media (middle ear infection in both ears). I gave my patient a penicillin injection, a sedative, and was then to my astonishment given a resounding kiss on the cheek by the middle-aged lady. I pretended to show no surprise, but as I bent down to put my stethoscope in my case I felt her hand poked into the inside pocket of my overcoat.

I had already established in my mind what kind of a house I was in and thought it wise not to make any comment. I was terrified the middle-aged lady might insist that I accept the services of one of her girls as a reward for my services and prayed that I would be allowed to leave the house without mishap. Luckily, no inducement was offered to me to remain, but when I got into my car after being waved goodbye by the ladies and felt into my pocket, I found two, large, white, crisp, important pieces of paper. They were five-pound notes! I must admit when I got back home that morning I examined my pieces of good luck very carefully, I had never previously had the good fortune of owning a five-pound note.

I telephoned Dr Gordon, whose practice was in Burdett Road, who was the patient's general practitioner, in the morning, to tell him of the diagnosis and the treatment I had given to his patient – in case he wanted to revisit. In the course of conversation I mentioned the fact that some money had been put into my pocket whilst in his patient's house.

'My! My!' was his retort. 'What a lucky fellow you are! Do you know what house you went to? You have been to the *holy of holies* in the docks. You must be one of the few select men who have actually taken money from "Madam" instead of giving it. She must certainly have taken a liking to you. I would frame the money if I were you. It will never happen again'.

At that time, because of the long hours I worked, the need to make a living and build up my own practice, I had frequent attacks of migraine. I have already mentioned I worked for a ten-doctor rota; not all the doctors however had the accommodation for me to be able to spend the night at their premises when it was their turn to be on duty. On these occasions, I had to do the visits from my own home in Peckham; this meant travelling to and from the East End all through the night.

On the evenings when there was no accommodation available for me to sleep over, I often took a friend, Mark Ormonde, to accompany me to overcome the boredom. I have known Mark since my student days. He came just for the ride and I used to phone home from the East End to find out whether any more visits had come in whilst I had been away. They never did – until I arrived home again. Bleepers and mobile phones incidentally had not yet been invented.

On leaving the East End after one very-bad night

and travelling alone, I almost collapsed at the wheel of my car at the exit of the Rotherhithe tunnel with a blinding headache. I had already been through the tunnel eight times that night. At four o'clock in the morning I could go no further without a rest. I stopped the car and laid my aching head on the steering wheel. Before I had even time to take a cigarette from my pocket – I was a thirty-a-day cigarette smoker at the time – I was dragged out of the driving seat into the passenger seat by four very strong arms.

'It's funny,' I heard a deep gruff voice say, 'his breath doesn't smell.'

When I realised who my persecutors were – the police – I told them who I was and what my problem was. Policemen can be very human when the necessity arises, one of them drove me home in my car while the other chap followed in the police car.

I worked for this group of doctors for two years, but my period of night rota duties ended abruptly at 2.30 one February morning, in 1955, when I walked out of a doctor's premises in St Leonard's Road, Bow.

I had been doing house calls all evening and was dog-tired when I finally managed to crawl into bed at this doctor's surgery. The housekeeper occupied the flat above the surgery but a back bedroom had been retained – rather the housekeeper allowed me to use it – when I was on duty. For some inexplicable reason, whenever I was on duty for this doctor I spent the whole evening going to and fro from the surgery. There always appeared to be a nonstop supply of visits to keep me busy. I was usually so exhausted at the end of the night shift that had the bed been a bed of nails I would have probably sunk into it and fallen asleep. The sheets were always greyish, the mattress sunk almost to the floor, but who worried? It was better than driving home and possibly having to drive back to the East End, again, again, and again.

I got into this cold, freezing bed in the St Leonard's Road surgery, but although exhausted, the cold prevented me from falling asleep immediately. In bed, as I started to get warm, I began to feel itchy. I always went to bed in these doctors' surgeries stripped down to my vest and pants. I never bothered to take pyjamas. I now thought the intense irritation which I felt all over my body must be due to the cold and the rough blankets. Perhaps, I thought, I had an allergy to the washing powder with which I hoped the sheets had been washed.

I began to scratch. I scratched and scratched. I scratched my arms, my body, my legs: I just could not stop scratching. In desperation, to have a good scratch, I threw off the covers. It made no difference. I got out of bed and switched on the light. I nearly fainted! What met my eyes made me feel sick. The bed was full of bugs. I was being eaten alive! I was furious!

Two pounds a night for ten doctors was, even in the fifties, not exactly being overpaid. To be used also as food for their pets was just too much!

I dressed and left the surgery and that East End rota in a hurry – never to return. I never even said goodbye to the housekeeper. I could not get home quickly enough. I arrived home at three in the morning. My family who had not been expecting me home until eight o'clock came running scared into the bathroom. They thought a dirty intruder had entered! They could hear the noise of splashing and groaning.

It was bedbugs swimming for their lives as I splashed them off my body whilst I lay immersed in the bath!

* * *

Peckham has always been noted for its supply of *wide boys*, confidence tricksters, and criminals, both of the crass and petty types. Perhaps, to give me a trial run, I had the experience of being given a lesson in the first week of my settling down in the area. The interesting thing was, the chap who gave me the lesson had – until he came into my home – never been to Peckham.

In 1952, while working in Lavender Hill, Battersea, as an assistant to Dr Heyman, prior to my move to Peckham, I had made friends with a patient, Harry Armstrong, who was a painter and decorator. The friendship had commenced and blossomed by my frequent meetings with his wife who was the local district nurse.

Harry appeared to be excited when I told him that I had made up my mind to branch out on my own and be my own boss. He did not have too high an opinion of my employer. To be honest, he hated him. My boss lived in a Chelsea Mews house and had asked Harry to do some repair work on the property, but when Harry arrived at the scene he found another builder was already there. As Harry explained to me, he had only been asked the previous week and it was not that he had kept my boss waiting. Dr Heyman, infinitely more experienced – he was after all thirty years older than I was – had gone home after asking Harry, had thought the matter over and regretted asking him. He had forestalled Harry by arranging for another builder to commence work before Harry had even put his ladders up. Harry offered to decorate my surgery in Peckham at cost and with money being tight I had no hesitation in accepting his offer. He started work on January 22nd 1953, the date is etched into my brain. I have never forgotten the date! It was the day when I had my first experience of a confidence trickster. It cost me a lot of money which, at that time, I could ill afford.

The first evening, after he had spent a day at work in the back upstairs bedroom, he asked me for some money. He wanted to buy filler, size, sandpaper and other odd items so that he could complete the job. He made the excuse that as he was doing the work at cost he had no more money to buy material and had run out. I gave him a five-pound note, a lot of money in 1953.

He turned up on the following day, spent the whole day in the same room and carefully locked it up after him. His excuse for locking it was that he didn't want my youngster getting himself all mucky playing with the materials in the room. Before leaving, he again asked for money: he asked for ten pounds as he knew a chap who had some paint 'going cheap'. He was going to see the chap on his way home, he hoped he was not already too late and that it had not been snatched up. After all, a bargain like this did not fall into one's lap every day.

It had not taken my friend the builder long to find out that I was a *gullible halfwit,* a sucker, just waiting to be taken to the cleaners. All I was now doing was trying to prove him right! I foolishly parted with the ten pounds as if he was doing me the biggest favour in my life.

He came back the next day, then not until 10.30 in the morning, and made a point of disturbing me during my surgery consultations to show me a small tin of peach paint which he said was a sample of the load he had successfully bought the previous night from his friend. He apologised for turning up late but he had been to collect the stuff and, as I could see for myself, he only bought top quality. He spent the whole day in the same back bedroom again, locked it afterwards, and before leaving told me what I found out later to be one more of his fictitious tales. Fictitious they are as I write about them today: at the time, young and inexperienced, trying to cut corners in making ends meet and improve the practice property, I was the perfect idiot waiting to be taken for a ride by an expert confidence trickster. My friend was such a charming fellow. I am glad he did not enter my life at a later date, otherwise, I would certainly have found myself in the bankruptcy court.

Harry told me, when on the previous night he

had gone to collect the paint from his friend he had met a roofer and tiler in the house. He knew I had problems with my roof and his friend the roofer would be prepared to do the necessary work for me at cost, as a favour to him. He owed Harry a favour, and what better way to repay the debt than to do the work for me. In the course of conversation with the roofer he had mentioned the fact that he had not yet bought the paper for the rooms in my house and asked him if he knew anyone who had some paper going cheap. I would not believe what the chap said! We were so phenomenally lucky!

The owner of the house on which the roofer was at present working in Kensington had bought wallpaper for his house, but his wife did not like it. There had been blazing rows over the paper: in the end the boss had given way and ordered a different pattern. He now had a load of paper to get rid of. This paper, really the best money could buy – it had to be for a Kensington job – was now going for a song. He and his friend had worked out the measurements, it was enough to do my whole surgery and would be enough to do my living accommodation too. It was a bargain: an offer we could not refuse: we would never get a chance like this again. It is surprising really how I became mesmerised by the phrase, *'We will never get a chance like this again'*. I believed him. After all, I was going to get enough wallpaper to do the whole house. I parted with forty pounds.

He came back on Thursday and said that he would not now come back until after the weekend as he had some plumbing to do for a friend who needed his expert advice. They had to make a start on the job on Friday so that his friend could work through the weekend and finish the job by Monday morning. He would bring the roofer with him after the weekend.

At eight o'clock, on a cold, January, Monday morning, there was a smiling Harry at the front door of 105 Bellenden Road, accompanied by a roofer who had a grin which extended from ear to ear. Harry, after the necessary introductions went upstairs to his hideaway in the back bedroom: his friend the roofer put up his ladders and went on to the roof. Within ten minutes the roofer was down with his report. The zinc valley gutter was cracked and needed replacement. Some slates were missing from the roof, if I did not replace the valley gutter immediately more slates would be dislodged and the house would be flooded with the next downpour! He scared me to death! I gave him twenty pounds to go immediately and buy a new valley gutter and replace the missing slates: he left on the understanding that he would return at first light on the following day. So as not to get in the way of patients – his ladders were an obstruction to my front door – and not to encourage a burglar, he took away the ladders with him. *I have not seen him, his ladders, or my twenty pounds again!*

Harry spent that whole day, Monday, working in the same upstairs back bedroom: to be fair, he did not disturb the roofer examining the roof once! However, before I commenced my evening surgery he waylaid me again and asked for more money. He really was a master in his profession – confidence trickster not painter and decorator – he knew exactly when to time his intrusions, when I would be most vulnerable. He said that he had met yet another chap in the pub, who had enough paint to do the outside of the house. This fellow had enough for the whole outside for the paltry sum of twenty pounds. If I was prepared to buy this, he would have in his possession enough material to do both the inside and outside of the whole house. It was a snip! A bargain! He once again used the hypnotic phrase, 'We will not get a chance like this again'.

Harry, by his trickery, had now left me almost penniless. I could only give him ten pounds, even then I felt obliged to apologise at not being able to give him more. Ten pounds, he said, would only buy half the amount required, but as a favour to me he was going to take it, in no way was he going to turn down a bargain offer. He took it with the remark, 'at least it will be enough to get on with'. What he really meant was, you have no more money, I have no further use of your friendship.

He did not come back on the following day, but as I had a friendly relationship with him, I was not terribly worried. I knew where he lived, it was winter, and I thought that perhaps he had been called away to another job; to do some emergency plumbing. When he did not appear for two weeks I went to see him; he had taken the key of the back bedroom with him and I did not want to be forced to break open the door and ruin the lock. I had reached the state in my finances when I did not have enough money to call in a locksmith or a carpenter.

I went to his flat, over a shop in Queenstown Road, Battersea, the Lavender Hill end, and his wife answered the door. Her husband, she told me, was not in, but she was very friendly and invited me in for a cup of tea while we waited for him to return. I accepted her offer and we had a pleasant chat. He had still not returned after our 'tea party' and she promised to tell him to get in touch with me as soon as he got back. Harry, she told me, was out on an emergency plumbing job, but something must have gone terribly wrong. He had told her before he left that he would be back in an hour and he had now been away for six hours. She had no idea where he was and rather than outstay my welcome, I left.

'I promise to get him to telephone you as soon as he gets back,' she said.

When I recall the succession of events, I should not have been surprised at not receiving a telephone call. Firstly, he had taken all my money and he knew it: secondly, he did not have a telephone so he would have had to trouble himself and go to a call box. Whether the wife knew of her husband's trickery I never found out, but after waiting three weeks for a telephone call which never came, I went to Battersea again. Harry answered the door himself and he greeted me like a long-lost brother with a tale which almost reduced me to tears.

After leaving my surgery in Peckham, on that fateful Monday evening, he had gone home on a Number 37 bus. He had jumped off the bus near Clapham Common but had misjudged his landing. He had fallen straight into the path of a following motorist who had made it his duty to knock him down.

'No!' he had not been knocked unconscious, he had just sustained eight fractured ribs, a fractured collar bone, a broken arm and a fractured ankle. He had been taken to hospital by ambulance and kept in for a few days. He was such a good actor: I must be some sort of an idiot: I believed him! In retrospect, I do not remember when having tea with his wife, a nurse, she had mentioned anything about an accident to me. She would certainly have done so if only to ask my medical opinion on the prognosis after his accident. It had only been five weeks since I had previously seen him and he certainly showed no signs in his gait or arm movements that he had ever been involved in an accident.

He explained that the only reason he had not yet returned to work was that he had been attending hospital for physiotherapy. His friends, from whom he had bought the materials for my surgery, had been storing the goods for him. As he had not been fit to return to work, they had not delivered the materials. Now, as I could see for myself, he was back to his normal self. He had in fact been in touch with his friends that very day, just before I had called, and asked them to deliver the paint and paper so that he could start work again. He was determined to complete the job as a favour to me and I could count on his charges being reasonable. I should have no fear, as soon as the materials were in his possession he would be back at work.

I asked for the key to my back bedroom as I wanted to open the window and dry the place out and without hesitation he gave it to me. He had it in his pocket. I could see from this, he said, he intended to come back to work as soon as he had something to work with. He however did not explain what the other twenty-or-so keys in his pocket from which he had extracted mine were doing. On leaving, he said he knew a chap who had some gardening tools going cheap. For ten pounds, I could have two forks, two spades of different sizes, a lawn mower with a grass box, two hoes, and he would throw in a dibber for good measure. It was an offer which only a fool could turn down! The mesmerising phrase – *we would not get a chance like this again* – reappeared. Time however must have immunised me against the phrase, it did not have the same effect on me as on previous occasions. He would bring the gardening tools with him when he came back to work, he said.

Providence told me not to give him a penny, but on the pretence of trying to find some I searched my pockets. I found only one-miserly-pound note which I told him I needed to buy petrol for my journey home and pretended to be devastated. It was my turn to box clever: I still wanted him to come back and give me some value for all the money which I had laid out. If he brought the gardening tools with him when he came to the surgery I told him, I would go straight to my bank and get the money. The chap who had the gardening tools would obviously trust him! We parted the best of friends. His final words on my leaving were, he was dying to commence work again and could not wait to get back.

When I got back with the key that day, I could not get to the back bedroom quick enough. I ran up the stairs, opened the back bedroom door, and in my haste to see how far he had got with his decorating failed to see the greasy rag which was on the floor at the entrance. I slipped. I nearly broke my neck as I hurtled across the room into the windowsill. The room was empty. There were no tools in the room. No distemper, no filler, no size, just the greasy rag and a miserable weather-beaten old hammer, which I still use to this day. The only work Harry had done in the room was, the walls had been scraped and made good. They were so good, they were mirror like in their smoothness. He had obviously had time to kill in the few days he had been in my house, he had spent it filling in all the holes in the walls and smoothing down.

It is almost an insult to my reader's intelligence to add that my friend's promises were not fulfilled and he did not return to work again. After waiting a further two months, I went back to his flat. I was now told by his wife that her husband was in hospital with pulmonary tuberculosis and I am certain she was telling me the truth. I only hoped working in my closed back bedroom had not made a contribution to his illness. On returning to Queenstown Road, to see how he was about three months later, the lady who answered the door told me that the couple from whom she had acquired the flat had moved.

Over forty years have passed since I last saw Harry. If any reader knows the gentleman about whom I have written this story, I would be grateful if he or she would get in touch with me. I still have a practice at the same address in Peckham. *If Harry will agree to give me my money back, I will return his hammer.*

*   *   *

Experience is a commodity which cannot be bought or taught. In the normal person it can be likened to a bud which in the fullness of time grows, blossoms, then fruits. Experience in medicine is no exception to the general rule. It is only gained from years in practice and lacking it cost me dearly when I was called out to see a butcher in Ivanhoe Road, in 1958.

With more experience I would have realised that the owners of a butcher's shop which was firmly established, which had been in the possession of the Moseleys' since the thirties, was always full of customers, would have been worth a *bob-or-two*. I knew this shop had an excellent name, the owners served in it themselves and I also knew that the meat sold in it – although I could not personally vouch for it – was reputed to be of excellent quality. What this should have taught me, the owners were not as poor as the proverbial church mice I thought them to be.

I was called out at 8.30 pm one night in December 1958, by one of the Moseleys' neighbours, who had run into my surgery asking me to visit Mr Moseley urgently. The neighbour had no idea what had happened, he just knew that a breathless Mrs Moseley had knocked at his door and asked him to get me to come immediately as her husband had collapsed. I had answered the door myself, I had therefore no possible excuse not to go or make excuses to postpone the visit.

I tore myself away from our newly-installed television set, picked up my medical case, and with the neighbour in the passenger seat of my car made my way to the Moseleys to see what problem I had to solve. I remember it being an extremely-cold night and having left a nice, cosy, coal fire, feeling absolutely frozen when I arrived at the butcher shop. What shocked me however when I reached the Moseleys was to find the inside of the shop appeared to be colder than the outside! In the living room at the back of the shop I found Mr Moseley lying on the floor covered with a blanket: this room was no warmer than the shop. He was conscious, but could not speak coherently. His speech was slurred and he was only able to answer my questions with grunts. The left side of his face was paralysed, his mouth was distorted, and he could not move his left arm or leg. I had no doubt in my mind of the diagnosis – poor old Mr Moseley had suffered a stroke.

On being told the diagnosis Mrs Moseley appeared to show no surprise: old people as a general rule accept illness readily: it is expected. The surprise came afterwards – it was mine! Mrs Moseley insisted that her husband be admitted into a private room in King's College Hospital for treatment. She was adamant! She had no facilities for nursing him. As she explained, she herself was old and she did not have the strength to look after the old man. I offered to help, provide her with nursing care, but she was firm, there was no way she could nurse the old chap. Under no circumstances was she prepared to allow the fellow to remain at home. She would also not allow him to go into an ordinary ward in hospital, he was going to be a private patient. As an afterthought, she added, **'someone has to look after the shop!'**

From the way this couple lived, from the conditions at the back of their shop, I had always regarded this couple as being extremely poor, just able to scratch a living. Her insistence therefore on having her husband put into a private bed in the hospital rather startled me. Their living conditions were deplorable. Even the premises of the poor young doctor in Bellenden Road, struggling to make a living, was palatial compared to theirs. I wondered whether she realised what the cost was going to be, what their financial position would be like after a prolonged hospital stay. My own belief was, they would probably have to sell the shop to pay the bill!

Lighting in their premises was with gas mantles. Electricity had not been installed. Hot water was only available by boiling kettles. There was no bathroom. For personal washing, there was an old-fashioned crock washbasin in the bedroom with a crock jug inside it. I imagine that if they ever needed a bath they went to the public baths in Camberwell. The furnishings in the living accommodation both in the upstairs' and downstairs' rooms were poor and dilapidated and contained the barest of essentials. Even the floors seem to point out the family's poverty. There was old linoleum on the floor and this had worn through in parts: where this had occurred the wooden floorboards – which at some time had been stained – could be seen.

No general practitioner in these circumstances could himself have taken the responsibility of sending this man into hospital into a private room. I therefore asked Dr Gilpin, a medical consultant at King's College Hospital, one of my old teachers, to visit Mr Moseley privately at home that same night. I had great respect for my old teacher and knew, besides being an excellent diagnostician, he would have the experience to discuss with Mrs Moseley the financial arrangements. He would also have the necessary authority to explain to her the cost which would be involved in having a patient admitted for a long stay into the private wing of a prestigious hospital such as King's.

Dr Gilpin, a most charming man, a man who commanded respect even by his appearance, examined Mr Moseley, and agreed after a lengthy conversation with his wife to admit him into one of his beds in the private wing of King's. In our discussion however, after he had seen how the Moseleys lived, he was – to say the least – a little unhappy to have agreed to accept Mr Moseley as a private patient. He wondered if the means to pay the hospital bill would be available, whatever Mrs Moseley said. He was not worried over his own account, the hospital however did not look kindly on consultants who had patients admitted to the private wing and then expected the hospital to foot the bill. He had in his conversation with Mrs Moseley suggested that she allow her husband be admitted into one of his NHS beds in the hospital. She had steadfastly refused. He had reinforced his argument diplomatically by telling her that the cost of a private bed was astronomical, was not really worth it with Mr Moseley's complaint. She had however been adamant. She only wanted him in a private room! He would therefore admit him for a week or two and see what transpired. If the hospital bill was not paid at the proper time he was sure the matron would see to it that Mr Moseley was transferred into a public ward.

I ordered an ambulance immediately after Dr Gilpin left and Mr Moseley was duly taken into the private wing of King's College Hospital that same night. He remained in the hospital private wing for twenty-seven weeks. It must have cost a fortune!

I had not known the Moseleys all that well and twenty-seven weeks is a long time for a doctor and a patient to be parted. To be honest, I had forgotten all about the chap, when I received a request one day in August 1959, to visit Mr Moseley, in a private house in Lordship Lane, Dulwich. This was to a house, on the same side, and a few doors away from Dulwich Library.

The Moseleys, unbeknown to me, in the time that Mr Moseley had been in hospital, had sold their butcher shop and bought this house in Dulwich. Although I had gone through Ivanhoe Road daily in my car and passed their butcher shop, it had never been shut. I had not heard from anyone about them, and presumed Mrs Moseley had been carrying on the business as usual. I had kept well away from them. I believed Mrs Moseley had made a dreadful mistake in allowing her husband to be treated in the private sector. I did not want to be asked to share the bill of costs! The request for a visit from outside my immediate practice area did cause me to think twice as to whether to accept it, but after all, the Moseleys were elderly and I felt sorry for the old lady. I went.

This is where my lack of experience told. It caused me later to regret that I had been made a fool of, perhaps made a fool of is not the right expression; used, may be more correct. I might, if I had had more experience, have become a rich man! I should have insisted at the time, if the Moseleys wanted me as their general practitioner there was only one way I was prepared to accept them, as private patients. Perhaps, I should not now blame myself too much. I was not completely at fault. Mrs Moseley, when she telephoned for the visit, did indeed stipulate that she wanted me to keep them on as my NHS patients. At the time, I thought the long stay in hospital had ruined them! They had probably run out of money and I did not have the heart to tell her to find a doctor nearer to them. I stupidly kept them on my list.

Mr Moseley had not recovered his speech and now that Mrs Moseley had moved away from the area in which her business had been situated she had no one to talk to. The business had occupied their lives, twenty-four hours a day, and having made no friends, I was one of the few people she knew with whom she could have a friendly relationship. Visiting elderly patients regularly has always been a normal part of my practice routine, but at that particular time I was even more keen to do so. I had only been in practice a few years and wanted to get known. I therefore visited the Moseleys weekly for about two years when Mrs Moseley, without warning, without any previous history of heart trouble, had a heart attack and died.

In the two years in which I had been making regular weekly visits I had never met anyone in the house who had any family connection with them. I knew the Moseleys were childless, Mrs Moseley had often mentioned this fact to me, and in all our conversations she had never spoken of any family. No one, except their solicitor who visited them regularly, appeared to show interest in their welfare. Their solicitor got in touch with me as soon as he knew of Mrs Moseley's demise and arranged for a live-in housekeeper for Mr Moseley. I arranged for a district nurse to take care of the nursing side of his problems as he had a bed sore. To all intents and purposes Mr Moseley's life style at first appeared to be unchanged, indeed, for a short time I thought he enjoyed being a widower. He then became increasingly depressed. He had – in the two years I had been visiting him – become more and more immobile, and a man in his eighties who has had a stroke is not a suitable candidate for active home physiotherapy. After his wife's death he became a complete vegetable. Whereas, previously, his wife had taken him out for walks in his wheelchair, his housekeeper now refused to do so. When I suggested to the fellow that a breath of fresh air might do Mr Moseley good, I was brusquely told it was not part of his terms of contract to push a fat old man in a wheelchair and give himself a rupture in the process.

Poor old Mr Moseley was got out of bed in the morning, placed into his wheelchair, and allowed to remain there like a *stuffed goose* all day. He could not move by himself. His eyesight was too poor to read. He could not speak. When he wanted something, he made a grunting noise. There was nothing at all he could do. He just spent day after day sitting in one position. Even a caged bird enjoys more freedom. It was therefore no surprise, as he was so immobile that sooner or later he would suffer an attack of bronchopnuemonia. He had no wish to live, and it was obvious from the first day of the attack my efforts to cure him would fail. Destiny then played her hand! Exactly one year to the day of his wife's death he left this life to join her.

I had now been a regular visitor to the Moseley house, in Dulwich, for three years. The number of visits I had made had run into hundreds, and the only reward I had ever received was a cheap bottle of Cyprus sherry at Christmas. On the day of Mr Moseley's death I was asked by his solicitors – who were also his executors – to call at the house to sign the necessary documents for cremation. Mrs Moseley had been cremated and this presumably had been his wish too. I went to the house after morning surgery and was met by the housekeeper who had to force a path for me through a crowd of mourners to take me to his room so that I could sign the necessary forms. I was thunderstruck at the number of people in the house.

'What gives with all the people?' I asked.

'They are all his relatives,' was the reply.

They had been informed by the solicitors of Mr Moseley's demise and had come to pay their last respects. It did not now take much mental effort on my part to realise that our poor Mr Moseley had not died penniless. His wife indeed had been right in buying comfort for her husband when he had first suffered his stroke. Inexperienced as I was, I could not understand why the family had not thought it worthwhile to attend when Mrs Moseley had died.

The *coup de grâce* however came about a year later. The firm of solicitors, in Streatham, who dealt with the Moseleys' affairs when they had been alive, telephoned me at the surgery and asked me to send in my account for my medical services – by return of post. I was reprimanded! I was told by the solicitor on the telephone that I was negligent in not sending in my account. It was now over a year. My account was holding up the winding-up of Mr Moseley's estate!

I explained to the chap on the telephone that there was no account to settle, the Moseleys had always been my National Health patients. There was dead silence for a minute. I thought the line had gone dead. It was shock! Peels of laughter then followed: even the solicitor now lost his cool.

'Bloody hell! Do you know the buggers haven't left you anything!' he said.

He went on to explain that the Moseleys had

been millionaires. The butcher shop had been in the family for generations, had just been something for the Moseleys to do to keep them out of mischief. It only just paid its way. The Moseleys' income came from rents from Du Cane Court and other blocks of flats which they owned in Streatham. They also owned houses which they rented out in various parts of London.

My inexperience had cost me a fortune!

*　*　*

I had only been in practice a few weeks before I had my first experience of treating a patient who was not registered with me as one of my NHS patients. It was 2.30 am in May 1953, when I opened my front door to an extremely-noisy man who rang my front door bell and kept his finger on the bell push so that there was going to be no escape from attending to his wishes. His wife, he told me, had collapsed with abdominal pain and he demanded an immediate home visit. The couple only lived in Chadwick Road, so I put on some clothes over my pyjamas and walked up the road with the fellow.

I examined his wife, found that she was suffering from gall bladder colic, gave her an injection to ease her pain, and told her husband that I would call back later, after morning surgery, to see what the condition of his wife was. I explained to the chap there was no point in getting his wife into hospital at that time in the morning. She would only be left in the ward until the specialist called later on that day; even then she might be sent straight home. It would be far better to wait until after I had done my morning surgery, we would then be in a position to have a much clearer picture of his wife's prognosis. If the pain had not eased by that time, she would definitely require hospital admission for investigation. This advice took place at the front door as I was leaving and he listened to me respectfully and attentively. As I was ready to say goodbye, he politely told me not to take the trouble of calling again; he would call his own doctor out later on in the morning! I was dumbstruck! I then irately asked why he had not called out his own doctor to attend his wife rather than disturb me.

'Well,' he answered, 'my own doctor is Doctor Cohen: he hates being called out at night. He has to get his car out. He was furious with me the last time I called him out at night. He shouted at me for not getting him out earlier in the day. When I saw the red light over your front door, I thought it would be much more civilised if I asked you to come.'

I already knew his own doctor by reputation. He practised single-handed in Southampton Way, and although I had spoken to the fellow on a number of occasions I had never actually met the chap.

The red light over the porch leading to the front door was a luxury which I introduced immediately after we moved into the surgery premises. I intended it to be an advertisement, but it proved an embarrassment almost from the first day. We had only been in the house one week when the door bell rang at eight o'clock one evening. When I answered the door, whom should I see standing in the porch but a Frenchman pointing to the light. Without blinking an eyelid he asked for *'Mimi'*. He stood there, a beret on his head like a Breton onion seller, expressionless, no smile on his face to make me believe that he was a prankster, and kept repeating in a genuine French accent:

'How much is *Mimi?'*

Only a fool would not have realised immediately what his hopes were! We had been expecting my wife's cousin Esther who was bringing her husband to visit us. We had never met him as she had married him whilst I was stationed in Germany in the Forces. All my efforts to tell the fellow there was no *Mimi* on the premises were proving futile, he just kept pointing to the light. As he appeared not to understand English and he spoke French so quickly that my schoolboy French did not allow me to understand a word, I was becoming more and more frustrated. The impression I got was, he was not prepared to take NO for an answer. He was determined to come into the house. I was just as determined to keep him out. When I had reached the stage of intending to shut the door in his face, I was distracted by peals of laughter to his right, just out of my line of vision. It was a girl's laughter. It turned out to belong to Louise's cousin Esther, and the Frenchman was her husband Jacques. I had known that she had married a soldier, but had not known that he was a Frenchman who had served in the Free French Forces. The red light had given them an exceptional opportunity to play games.

It was not unusual to practise single-handed in the fifties, indeed most doctors did, and almost all practices were run by male doctors. The doctor's wife played an important part in running the practice, besides bearing his children and caring for his general needs, she acted as his secretary and *girl Friday*. An essential element of running a practice was to have the premises occupied twenty-four hours a day. If the doctor himself did not live on the premises he was duty bound to provide a housekeeper to live in and take messages. When I reminisce, I wonder what a young doctor would think when I state that it was not essential for a doctor to have a telephone when I commenced in Peckham! Group practices too were few and far between: the only one in the Peckham area which I can remember was the Hilton and Speirs group, in Commercial Way.

Doctor Cohen was, as I was at the time, a single-handed practitioner. He was a bachelor, in his sixties, an Irish Jew, who played solo. And although he was not a regular synagogue attender the members of his card school were. I often had evening calls from his patients as he was never to be found in the evening, but his excuses after I rang him on the following morning were always the same. He had been called out urgently to an address in New Cross. What he forgot to add was, there was a game of solo taking place there. Dr Cohen, for all his faults, had the Irish blarney. His patients forgave him all his trespasses.

In January 1958, the evening surgery went on and on, it appeared to be never ending. I had already seen twenty-nine patients, and the little old lady sitting at the end of the waiting room was still there. I had no appointment system in those days, and not previously having had the pleasure of seeing this smiling face assumed that she had come to be registered as a new patient. I had almost built up my practice from scratch, Dr Morgan, my predecessor, had only bequeathed me two-hundred patients. I knew every one of them: this sweet old lady would not have escaped my notice.

Patients came in to see me then left, but she still remained sitting in a chair, smiling pleasantly. The time was now 8.30 pm, it was a bitterly-cold night, the street door had been closed for an hour and I was thankful that at least no more patients could come in. After I had seen one of my last patients out and made sure the front door was firmly closed I went into the waiting room to call in my next patient. It was then I noticed that she was the only one left. She had been in the room since the front door had been opened – since five o'clock. I beckoned her to come in, but she did not notice my signs: she was too busy tidying up the magazines, some probably as old as herself!

'You can come in now,' I said. There was still no response. Believing her to be deaf I now shouted to her to come in. This at last produced a reaction.

'Shall I put the fire out?' she said.

'You can come in now,' I repeated, as she now condescended to look at me.

'I don't want to see you,' she answered.

'I am not one of your patients. I am a patient of Dr Cohen's. He is a lovely man. He doesn't do a surgery on Thursday night so I came in here for the company, to have a chat, and keep warm. I will tell him what a nice man you are too when I see him on Monday.'

One evening, in the spring of 1959, when the daffodils and tulips were in season and allergic conditions at their height, I was called out to a patient of Dr Cohen's, in Lyndhurst Way, just around the corner from the surgery. This patient, a lady in her mid-fifties, was having an acute asthmatic attack. I had to spend one-and-half hours of my precious time with her, giving her adrenaline 1/1000 by subcutaneous injection – one minim, per minute. She thankfully recovered completely and the joy at my success on allowing his wife to breathe again could be seen on her husband's face. He was so overcome, he insisted that I take a bottle of whisky to drink his wife's health when I got home. I took the bottle. It would have been churlish of me to refuse!

I rang Dr Cohen on the following morning to inform him what I had done for him on the previous evening and the words of thanks I received were, 'thanks for seeing Mrs Wheeler for me last night, old boy. I will do the same for you one day. By the way, do you play solo?'

'Sorry, no!' was my prompt reply, although I do. I knew the stakes which his school were playing for were more than I could afford and I also knew that he had the reputation of being an expert. I did not want to be put in the position of doing his work then having to pay him for the privilege of doing so! I never ever received any recompense for attending his patients and it was only a few months after attending his asthmatic patient that I learned he had taken himself off for a long stay in his native Ireland.

At that time, my mother, who lived in Liverpool, was having problems with her ears, and I decided to visit her on my half-day. My half-day was Thursday afternoon and as I knew Dr Cohen's half-day was Wednesday afternoon, he would now have the opportunity of repaying me for all the work which I had done for him! I would ask him to act as locum for me and attend any patient of mine who required an emergency visit. As I could get no reply from his surgery by telephone I went round to knock on his surgery door. I rang the bell. I could hear the ringing tone, but no one answered the door. I knocked and knocked: still no answer. I turned to leave, when my attention was drawn to a notice which was stuck on the window to my right, presumably the waiting room. It read, *Dr Cohen is away on holiday. Arrangements have been made for his patients to be seen by Dr Baccaro, in East Surrey Grove. On his half-day, or should Dr Baccaro not be available, patients will be seen at Dr Crown's surgery at 105 Bellenden Road.*

The cheek of the man! He had not asked me or intimated to me at any time that he wanted me to act as his locum. I was determined that I would make him pay for his audacity when he returned, and went to his surgery every day, for two months, to confront him. Once again however he got the better of me! When I mentioned the fact to his solo friends one day that his surgery appeared to be empty and neglected, they looked at me in astonishment. Everyone, except me, apparently knew that Dr Cohen had decided to make his stay in Ireland a permanent one! He had retired!

He hadn't even thought me important enough to tell me!

2

Prostitutes

Joy was a twenty-two-year-old blonde, with big blue eyes, and a figure which drew the attention of any male who was normal and happened to be in the vicinity at the time. When I made her acquaintance again in Peckham in 1960 – I had already met this young lady once in Battersea in 1952 – she had a reputation in the area of being on the *game*. What made her a target for malicious gossip was that she was a flashy dresser and money in Peckham being tight, her figure-hugging and eye-catching ensemble stood out like a sore thumb.

Her height was disconcerting. She was about five-foot-nine inches tall and as I am only five-foot-six inches, it meant that I had to look up to her whenever she came in to the surgery. Her height was something which I had found unforgettable. She was the same girl I had previously seen when I had been working as an assistant to Dr Heyman, in Battersea, in 1952. The episode in which she had been involved had impinged itself on my memory to such an extent, even today, when I think about it, I cannot help but laugh.

Dr Heyman was a character, wore a bow tie at all

times, was always immaculately dressed, and peered at you over the top of his designer half-spectacles. He did not need any lessons as to how to work his assistants, he knew how – into the ground! He had an NHS list of over five-thousand patients which he attended from his practice premises in Lavender Hill, Battersea, but not satisfied with this, he also ran a private practice from a flat in Nell Gwyn House, Chelsea. He himself lived in Burnsall Mews, Chelsea, and as these mews houses were originally flats over stables, it is obvious there was no way he could have run a practice from this place.

The *happening* he had with Joy was only one of many which I enjoyed whilst working for this chap and I was only with him for eight months! One incident concerned a rival practice in one of the side roads off Lavender Hill, when the doctor begged Dr Heyman for the loan of his premises for one day. The story was, the doctor had entered his surgery at 9 am that morning, to find all his patients standing in the waiting room; the chairs had disappeared. He went into his consulting room to find his desk and all his furniture had gone too. When he appeared stunned, his patients had told him not to worry, the men who had taken his old furniture would be bringing in the new any minute. They had been told the doctor had ordered new to replace the old. The trouble was, he had not! It was just that the thieves had been so plausible and had used a furniture van for their trickery. It has to be remembered that the year was 1952, the war had not ended until 1945, furniture was in very short supply and at a premium. The thieves who had stolen the goods would have had a ready buyer even before the furniture had been stolen.

Dr Heyman practised from a small terraced house, the ground floor being his workshop, the rest of the house used by the housekeeper as her living quarters. His actual practice accommodation consisted of one, small, front room, always crammed to the doors with patients used as a waiting room, and a tiny consulting room behind it leading to a kitchen. There was no water in the consulting room and if the doctor wanted to wash his hands he had to go into the kitchen. Doctor Heyman smoked, not only did he smoke in his free time, he also smoked in the surgery when examining patients. This is how I remembered in 1960 having previously seen Joy. How could I forget it?

I had been in Dr Heyman's practice for exactly one hour. I was sitting in the learned doctor's consulting room as he demonstrated the way he wished his patients to be examined and treated, when in walked Joy as his next patient. He was sitting at his desk, she was kept standing. I now – after so many years have elapsed – cannot remember whether there was a seat for her or whether I had appropriated it. She complained that she had a cough, so he asked her to unfasten her blouse to give him an opportunity to examine her chest. She did as she was told, stood before us with her blouse half-undone, the bottom button still fastened, and her brassiere still in place.

Doctor Heyman had a cigarette in his mouth and as he leant forward with the stethoscope some of the ash from his cigarette decided to detach itself and land in her cleavage. Before my startled-eyes, without the examiner batting an eyelid, Doctor Heyman placed his hand between Joy's breasts to shake them about, to dislodge the *foreign body*. I just looked on speechless. Joy stood there and did nothing. The only one who said or did anything was Doctor Heyman who, without apologising or showing anything untoward had occurred, ordered her to take deep breaths – his stethoscope firmly planted on her chest. Needless to say, I did not take his examination of this patient as an example of how he expected his patients to be treated!

Joy had a bubbly personality which I have never associated with these ladies of pleasure and were it not for the fact that I had a visit to the house and seen its opulence, I would not have believed the rumours which were spread about her. She lived with her boyfriend and baby son of one year old in the basement flat of a terraced house, in Talfourd Road. Although the baby was her pride and joy, strange to relate she was never seen out with it. She was never seen to push the pram, she never prepared the baby's feeds or changed the napkins: the boyfriend did all these chores. He also did the cooking, changed the beds and did all the housework. As the neighbours were not slow to tell me, he walked around the flat with an apron firmly attached to his body all day! I had been on visits to the flat on numerous occasions to see the baby, but had always been entertained in the kitchen. Joy herself – on the rare occasions she was ill – always came to see me at the surgery.

The first time I had an occasion to visit her and actually see the rest of the flat was when she had a raging fever due to an attack of acute tonsillitis. Not only was she ill, she felt ill; too ill to come to the surgery. What met my eyes amazed me. The basement was an Aladdin's cave. There were Persian carpets – real ones not nylon imitation – on the floor. A crystal chandelier on the ceiling with matching lights on the walls. The occasional tables were onyx. Even the two telephones looked as though my month's income would not have covered their cost! The bed on which I examined this lady was a four-poster with curtained sides: I had never examined a patient in one of these before and have never since. The flat reeked of expensive perfume: it intoxicated me: I was not even a client!

Anyone who knew Peckham in those days would have known at once what her profession was, but what puzzled me, how she managed to lure clients to the area. She certainly did not look the type to walk the streets plying her trade. A few years later however I had my answer as to how she had made her living: the expression call girl came to be used in common parlance. I now understood how she had obtained her customers, but why she had found the necessity of owning two expensive telephones when one – in my opinion – would have been sufficient, I have never been able to determine.

The baby was definitely hers, it was the image of her. I am also certain that her boyfriend – the chap who lived with her – had nothing to do with the production! It bore no resemblance to him whatsoever. As if to prove the fact, the baby as it grew into childhood developed all the characteristics opposite to those of the live-in boyfriend. The baby was dark-skinned with a mass of black hair, whilst the live-in friend was fair-skinned with straw-coloured hair. To be candid, even at one year the baby appeared more masculine than his effeminate minder! I assumed the friend was Joy's pimp, though I had always been given to understand pimps were *macho*. This chap was irrefutably not a macho type of man, he had the high-pitched voice and gait which is associated with the wide-hipped opposite sex.

I attended this family for four years, when the little boy, now five years old, had an attack of measles. He had a fairly mild attack, it took its usual course and there were no complications. It was all over in three weeks. The rash and cough disappeared – so did they! According to the neighbours, on my last visit, the removal van had been ready to pounce the moment I had taken my leave. I have never heard from them again.

* * *

Carol was a girl from the West Indies, eighteen years old, slim, with jet-black hair, large dark-brown eyes, long eyelashes and a perfect figure. She was always well-groomed and dressed in the height of fashion. I assumed that she was a model. Her expensive outfits were unusual for a girl in Peckham, black or white, at that particular period of time and she had been a patient of mine ever since her parents had brought her with them into this country in 1958. I had watched her grow up from a pretty schoolgirl into a beautiful young lady and had often complimented her parents at the way they had managed to make a lady of their daughter. When Carol telephoned me one Friday morning, in 1969, just as I was completing a morning surgery to ask me to see and treat her boyfriend as a private patient I was only too happy to oblige.

On the telephone, she told me that her boyfriend whom she had recently acquired had some difficulty in passing water, so I agreed to see him before evening surgery that same day. I assumed, knowing her age, that the boy friend would be in his early twenties, perhaps in the thirties. How wrong I was!

You can imagine my surprise when at 3 o'clock in the afternoon Carol, accompanied by an immaculately-dressed white girl, half-dragged, half-carried in a fellow to see me, who looked as if he must have been in his late fifties. He was, they told me, a professor of biochemistry in Copenhagen, who had come to London to attend a conference. He was a short, thickset, dark man, with a belly which hung over the top of his trousers. His suit looked expensive, he wore a collar and tie; he certainly looked the professional type of chap the girls had so proudly boasted about when they had made the request for me to see him. He even wore a red carnation in his buttonhole and if it were not for the way this poor fellow was dragged into my consulting room, legless, he could have been classified as a dandy. There was no question however that he was a man of some importance as he had been booked to give the main lecture at this meeting. The girls had made sure that I would be suitably impressed by bringing in the timetable of the conference to prove it.

The University of Copenhagen had booked the gentleman into a hotel in the West End. What the university did not know was, my patient and her white friend – with the collusion of the hotel staff – worked from the hotel bar of this hotel. On reflection, why should the university have known? I had been in practice in London for eighteen years, one of the girls was even a patient of mine – I had not known!

The white girl, who shared the burden of carrying in the middle-aged professor I had never seen before, even though she informed me she shared lodgings with my patient in Copleston Road and had been there for six months. She had never bothered to register with a doctor as she had never been ill, but now – I suppose she was trying to humour me – she asked me whether I would be prepared to accept her on my NHS list.

The girls, it appeared, had managed to persuade the professor to leave his *posh* hotel and share their lodgings with them in Copleston Road. They had been successful in making him believe he would learn a lot more biochemistry in their *digs* than he ever would at the dreary conference. They were right! The girls were so beautiful his male hormones had gone berserk and taken over his brain! What his hormones had failed to tell him, it was not his body these girls were after, it was his wallet. Having succeeded in their mission of persuading the fellow to leave the hotel, they had now set themselves up as his best friends and by doing so, fleecing him.

My initial attempts to obtain a history from the man proved to be an impossible task. All I could get out of the fellow was, he had given his lecture, and he was now enjoying his stay in Peckham very much more than his stay in the hotel. He explained that he was an expert in biochemistry, he knew the diagnosis of his complaint, knew how he had contracted his urinary infection: he had only come to me, at the instigation of his friends, for treatment. Would I please prescribe a course of antibiotics. The professor was so inebriated, he was at times incoherent and I expected him to fall asleep at any moment. He was in such a state of intoxication, he was only kept in position on the chair in my consulting room by being propped up by a girl standing on either side of him. He never stopped talking, kept rambling on about the beauty of his two companions and how much pleasure they gave him. He embarrassed me by giving me graphic descriptions of their naked bodies, and invited me to come to their lodgings and see for myself. I must be honest, this embarrassment of mine did not appear to show on the faces of the girls as he went on and on in his drunken state.

How I wish I could speak Danish when sober as he spoke English when drunk!

His accent and lack of embarrassment reminded me of an incident which I had in the army in 1948. At the time, I was a Lieutenant in the Royal Army Medical Corps, stationed in Neumünster, Germany, and my wife Louise had not yet been given permission by the authorities to join me. The Norwegian Brigade had their headquarters in Neumünster and I had been invited by the Norwegian Medical Officer to a cocktail party in their officers mess. The party was for nine o'clock in the evening, and it was only an hour old before the Norwegian doctor was taken to his bed by some other officers. He was 'dead drunk' and making a fool of himself. His nurse, who for some reason I have never been able to fathom out was not Norwegian but Danish, latched herself on to me. Sometime after midnight, when the party began to break up, the nurse invited me back to her room for a *rest*. I declined her offer. I honestly cannot remember the excuse I used at the time, but it was not until much later I learned that I had not behaved 'as an officer and a gentleman'! Whenever I approached the girl afterwards she completely ignored me. She also made a point of *cutting me dead* whenever we met at a function. One day I asked her boss, the doctor, if he knew the reason for his nurse's sudden hatred of me and he looked at me in amazement. He had obviously never been told of the incident and he probably had never noticed her behaviour towards me. He was so infrequently sober. He did promise me however to make it his duty to find out, he owed me a favour as I had been instrumental in saving his skin. He was so rarely sober in the evenings, when the Norwegian general's wife had taken ill one night and the general sent for the doctor, the Norwegian adjutant had thought it wise to ask me to see her and make some excuse for the unavailability of their own medical officer. I had saved the fellow a court martial!

After my chat to the doctor about his nurse he made it his duty to come to see me in our officers mess the same day and I was shocked! He complained of my ungentlemanly behaviour towards his colleague! My refusal to accompany her on the night of the cocktail party had hurt her feelings. I had not fancied her, not found her sexually attractive. She had been spurned!

Even in 1948 the Danish attitude to sex was different to ours. I had the nonsensical task afterwards of going to the medical room in the Norwegian barracks and apologising to this girl for my lapse in behaviour. With tongue in cheek, I explained that I was newly married and my wife was expected to join me any day. The nurse might on the night have found me not to be the best of lovers and it would then have been most embarrassing when the nurse met my wife. She might have had to be honest and explain to my wife what a lousy lover she had had the misfortune to marry! I had not wanted to put her in that embarrassing position. Thank heavens the nurse's English was poor. She accepted my apology, we parted the best of friends and with the help of the Norwegian doctor polished off a bottle of Benedictine. I remember the episode quite clearly: how could I ever forget it! I still remember the hangover!

To return to the story of 1969, I examined the Danish professor, albeit with difficulty, and found that his diagnosis was correct: he did indeed have an urinary infection. I also found he had hypertension but he was not at all interested in this diagnosis, he was already having treatment from a doctor in Denmark for this. I found examining this chap was not the easiest task I would have wished. He was more interested in giving me the anatomical details of his newly-found girlfriends than his own anatomy. His behaviour, although giving me concern, did not appear to cause the slightest ripple of disquiet in his two friends. After all, he was a professor, and it is to say the least a little unusual to have an academic passing a specimen of urine in one's consulting room watched over by two beautiful young ladies!

Even trying to make conversation with him was impossible. He continually interrupted me, discoursing about the beauty of his two companions. He would, whilst I was questioning him about his symptoms, make a sudden lunge to grab one of the girls and put his hands under her blouse to caress her breasts. Even semi-drunk his sexual desire was not on hold! Neither girl showed the least resistance or emotion whilst this caressing took place. Every lunge, every caress, was obviously going to be added to his bill! Such was his condition after I had examined him, besides giving him a course of antibiotics, I also gave him an injection of parentrovite, a vitamin B derivative. This injection, I believed, would give him the strength to enable him to prolong his visit in our capital city and enjoy both its cultural and *physical amenities.*

After I had completed my examination and treatment and he had been redressed by the girls, one of the girls put her hand into the pocket on the inside of his jacket and took out his wallet. From this she removed a wad of notes and without even asking how much I intended to charge carefully peeled off four five-pound notes. She handed them to me with the remark,

'I hope this is enough'.

I did not have the heart to say she had paid too much! She then carefully replaced the wallet in his pocket and whilst doing so grabbed the professor's elbow with her other arm. With her friend's help, who had simultaneously grabbed the other elbow, they lifted the poor, now half-asleep fellow, out of the chair.

I have seen Carol on numerous occasions since this incident – my profession not hers – and have been able to learn of these girls' experiences with the Danish professor. She told me, she and her friend had been to Denmark several times after their visit to me to spend some time with the professor. He had been a wealthy man with a house in Copenhagen and a villa on the coast. She and her friend had always been entertained at the villa. He had always paid their fares and expenses and what seemed surprising to me they had also been introduced to his wife and family. Even more surprisingly, the family had treated them civilly!

About four years ago Carol told me that she would be taking no more trips to Denmark. The poor fellow had died of liver trouble.

I was really surprised he had lasted so long!

3

Affairs

Susan, was a twenty-five-year-old young lady, with a figure like a cottage loaf, and married to a fellow whom I was told by the neighbours was a hard working, industrious, electrical engineer. He spent a lot of his time working away from London, with a wife like Susan, I was not surprised. I never had the fortune to meet this chap, fortune is the operative word, I did not understand how a normal human being could have married such a foul-mouthed bitch as his wife. She worked as an assistant for the social services so had ample excuses to come and see me and give me work to do.

She had a son, two years old, and I was always being called out to visit this lad. He did have kidney problems, but she made it her duty to make me work for my money. She always sent for me with an urgent request to see the child at the most unsocial hours. In all the years in which she was my patient she only sent for me at a reasonable hour once, even then she could not behave civilly. It was after this visit I was forced to remove her from my medical list! She always preferred evening visits and never showed any remorse or concern or even gave me a word of thanks when she got me out of a warm bed, at three o'clock, on a cold winter's morning.

She lived in Lyndhurst Grove, in the middle floor of a three-storey house, her family lived in the immediate area too. Her mother lived in Vicarage Grove, in a house owned by the council, it looked fine from the outside, but the inside mom had successfully turned into a low-class brothel. Perhaps I am mistaken, whether in 1966 this was a brothel, or mom changed her men friends as often as I change my socks I never found out. What I definitely did know, Susan's dad, Tom, was in prison for having taken part in an armed robbery which had gone wrong. Whenever I had reason to call at the house in Vicarage Grove there was a different man living with mom.

Susan's parents were simple folk, never did anybody any harm. Dad had only been driving the getaway car in an armed robbery, then only as a substitute. The chap who should have driven the car had been taken ill with tonsillitis and Susan's dad had been *subpoenaed* by the gangsters to drive the vehicle: he himself was unarmed when apprehended. As he told me much later he had never owned a firearm, he would never have known how to use one even if given one.

Susan, however, was a different kettle of fish. She was a domineering character. She did not need a firearm to frighten off the opposition, her face and raucous voice were enough. Her dad, when he was finally released from prison in 1968, told me a story which I will never forget.

He came home after serving six years and

knocked at his door in Marmont Road where he had lived when he was first locked away. His wife had only visited him twice in all the years he had been in prison. She had pleaded that she could not spare the time, she could not leave their children; in this she could have been truthful. She had five other children besides Susan, all younger than Susan, one normal, two subnormal and another two always in trouble with the police. Indeed, on two occasions, I had actually been called by the police to visit the troublesome ones in Peckham police station when they had complained of being ill. They had been apprehended for some minor felony and due to appear before the magistrates on the following morning.

Tom knew the problems which his wife was facing, and as a simple man accepted all his wife's excuses at her not being able to visit him. Now, in his own home, he could get no answer to his knocking. Entrance however, even without a key, was not going to prove too much of a problem. Tom had not been an armed gangster, he had been a small-time burglar. In his mind he thanked his wife for having had the perspicacity of leaving the side window of the bathroom open. Letting himself into the house was therefore *a piece of cake*.

He had a wash and brush-up in the bathroom and went into the kitchen. His mind boggled: his wife had certainly come into some money whilst he had been away! There was a new fridge, a new washing machine, a new toaster and a new stainless steel sink. There had never been enough money when he had been around to achieve such luxuries.

Even the stove was different. He could have sworn that they had had an electric stove before he was put away, now a new gas stove stood in its place, but why worry? He went to the fridge, took out some cheese, made himself a sandwich, sat in an armchair, and waited for the family to appear. Strange, he did not remember having this type of armchair. The old one had been covered with a loose cover to hide the parts which were threadbare, this one was all leather. He slipped when he stretched himself in it. Why his wife had gone to the expense of buying something he was never going to be comfortable in was something he was going to discuss very forthrightly when she came back. He was so uncomfortable in this chair!

As he now felt tired he decided he would go upstairs and have a lie-down on the bed. He went from the room into the passage: now he did have a problem! Where the stairs had previously been, there was a locked door facing him. He looked at it inquisitively! The door facing him could only be opened by a Yale key, he could have sworn there had been no door there previously. He had `always had a large family, they had always needed plenty of rooms, of necessity there had always been an upstairs in every house in which he had lived. He now panicked! He had come to the wrong house! He rapidly collected his belongings, climbed out of the bathroom window; did an exit exactly as he had performed an entry and went around to the front of the house.

The number of the house was the same, there was however a difference; where previously there had been a single number there was now an A to the left and a B to the right. He was sure when he had been in Goldsmith Road that he had entered the right road. He was now not quite so certain. He went back to check the road sign at the corner of Goldsmith Road and Marmont Road: the sign definitely read Marmont Road. He went back to the house and the truth suddenly dawned on him, in his absence, the council had converted the house into two flats. It was always possible the top flat had been enlarged and his family had been moved to the top flat, he would now try his luck.

He rang the top bell and after what appeared to be an eternity a young woman came down the stairs to answer the front door. He looked at her without speaking. He had never seen her before. Without saying one word, he walked away. She had given him a look as if he had come from outer space as he stood there. He knew intuitively that it was useless to have a question and answer session with her. He was now in a right pickle! He decided to do what he had spent his whole life in not doing, going voluntarily to the police. He walked into the police station at the corner of Meeting House Lane and Peckham Road, to be met by the most friendly greeting he had ever had from a policeman in his life. The sergeant on duty – who had been in the same station for years – recognised him immediately and welcomed him like a long-lost friend. Tom, when he told his story said,

'if anyone had told me I would be pleased to see a policeman whom I knew, I would have said they were *crackers*!'

When the sergeant heard Tom's sad story, he felt so sorry for his old antagonist that he ordered some sandwiches and tea for him while he looked through his notes. Tom's sons had been arrested several times since Tom himself had been incarcerated and their address was in his files. The search proved much easier than the sergeant had originally thought, a police officer had arrested one of his boys the previous week and the boy had been put on probation. Tom was now told his family had moved while he had been away and his new address was in Vicarage Grove, Camberwell. Although the kindly sergeant offered to provide a car to take Tom to his new home, Tom preferred to walk.

'I did not want to appear at my door in a police car. I was upset that no one in the family had bothered to tell me they had moved and I wanted time to cool down,' he said.

Tom walked home. After all, Vicarage Grove is within walking distance of Peckham Police Station if one is fit, and Tom told me that he had kept himself fit, even when *inside*.

His arrival at the family home that evening was treated by his family with complete indifference. One of his daughters opened the door to him, said 'hello,' and wandered off. He could not remember whether she had even shown any signs of knowing who he was. He was now lost. He had never been in this house before. He stood in the corridor like a lost sheep trying to gather his thoughts as to what his next step should be. Suddenly, from the door to the right, at the end of the passage, he heard voices and a peal of laughter and he made his way to the place from where the sound had emanated. There was very little light in the corridor, he had to search for the knob to open the door, but a shaft of light from the keyhole indicated to him where the catch to open the door was located.

He opened the door furtively, and the first person he saw sitting at a table in the centre of the room was his wife, Patricia. Next to her, one on either side, was sitting a middle-aged man: Tom had never seen either of them before. One of his daughters was sitting at the table too, so were two of his dopey sons. What struck him most forcibly at that moment however was, all the occupants of the seats appeared almost equal in their dopiness. On the table were some items of food – when he told me the tale he could not remember what these were – but he counted at least eight bottles of cider and they had all been opened; the stoppers were lying on the table. There was also a bottle of gin and from the contents left in the bottle the people sitting round that table had not been averse to its taste.

His mind was in a whirl. He had had, to put it mildly, a somewhat hectic day! As he gazed at the scene in a confused state his wife, without any sort of greeting or surprise at his sudden appearance said:

'Pull up a chair and join us Tom.'

She had actually recognised him! In one moment Tom realised one basic fact. No one in that room was at all put out by his return to the fold. They could not have cared whether he was alive or dead. He could have been in prison for the rest of his *natural* for all the interest they showed. He supposed they were all under the influence of the demon drink: to be honest, at that moment, all his interest in returning home evaporated! Instinctively, he knew that there was no way he was going to get any sense out of the present company. The men on either side of his wife – to whom he had not even been introduced – were behaving in a most disgusting intimate way with her. This, the person he had married, who had not even had the decency to tell him the family had moved! This was too much!

Tom was an asthma sufferer, he had seen me a few times before he had become a guest of *her Majesty*. He now had an attack. He closed the door behind him and fighting for his breath, panting and wheezing, made his way to my surgery as best he could. He had never been a violent man, he had never hit anyone in his life and although angry at the treatment meted out to him by his nearest, and so-called dearest, would not have been able to bring himself to change his nature and become violent. He had an asthma attack himself instead. This is the reason I had the pleasure of seeing Tom, at 7.30 that evening, in June 1964, in what must have appeared to him to have been the longest day in his life.

His wheezing could be heard as he opened the front door of my surgery: it was so loud, I persuaded the patient whom I was attending at the time to go back into the waiting room whilst I ushered Tom into my consulting room. In any event, the patient I was seeing was my last, and as he could hear for himself the distress Tom was in he departed very quickly out of the building. Perhaps he thought he might have been asked to be of assistance and was scared. I gave Tom some adrenaline subcutaneously and within two minutes he had recovered enough to tell me the story which I have painstakingly recorded.

'I wonder if you could do me a favour doc and lend me a couple of quid' Tom said, when he had fully recovered from his attack.

'What for?' I asked.

'If you really want to know', he said, 'I met a fellow *inside* who lives in Dover. He begged me to go and live with him if I ever felt like it and I am going down. He's a bachelor. He's a lonely old bugger. We became such good pals, I promised I would go and see him as soon as I could. I can't think of a better time than now.'

'What shall I tell your family when I see them?' I asked.

'Tell them to rot in hell!' was the answer.

I peeled off three one-pound notes out of my wallet, quite a sum of money in 1964, and put them in Tom's hand.

'Now this is not a loan, it's a gift – I don't want the money back. Try to go straight. Best of luck.'

We shook hands and I have not seen Tom since. Tom is not his real name, but if in his seventies he reads this story and recognises himself from the description, I hope my three pounds were not wasted!

Tom's daughter, Susan, about whom I commenced to write at the beginning of the story was as unlike the other members of the family as one could possibly find. She was bright. She was, as I have already mentioned, an assistant in the social services. She was not averse however to getting mixed up in a punch-up in a pub when the occasion presented itself. Just as Tom was mild and inoffensive, she was loudmouthed and aggressive. It is always said, 'an apple does not fall far from the tree' with regard to family relationships. In Susan's case, nothing could have been further from the truth. She was rotten to the core!

When she called me out at three o'clock, one morning, for the hundredth time, to see young Larry, her son, with earache, my wife handed me the phone to see whether I could offer advice. I wanted, if at all possible, to save myself a visit. Susan spoke even before I had time to say 'hello'.

'Larry is crying with earache and I want you to come and see him now. If you don't come, I will take him to hospital and get you "crossed off"!'

We obviously did not have a happy relationship! We all have a cross to bear, she was mine: but as she was a member of a very large family I did not want all her family taking their illnesses elsewhere! It is strange really, when I look back at my notes and reminisce at events which took place over thirty years ago I cannot recollect ever having treated Susan herself. I certainly never had an occasion to treat her husband: I never met the chap: it was always young Larry.

She sent for me for the thousandth time, in June 1968, but wonder of wonders, it was at nine o'clock in the morning and her Larry had earache. 'No!' she could not bring him in, a visit after surgery however would be very convenient to her. I had not taken the message myself as it had been telephoned in after surgery consultations had already commenced. When I went into reception and saw Larry's medical card and the request in the visit box I just could not believe my eyes. Susan could wait for a visit to be done at the proper time, after surgery – impossible! I would happily have taken a bet at the time that my receptionist had got the wrong message. Susan was prepared to be reasonable and conform? Unthinkable! What in heaven's name had got into her!

There were no patients in the waiting room at 10.00 am for some unknown reason and as Lyndhurst Grove is just around the corner from the surgery I thought I would save myself an argument later on in the day if I went and saw Larry there and then. I got into my car and was at the house in two minutes flat. Repeated ringing of the bell and banging on the front door however appeared to bring no response. I had given up hope of the front door being opened and was in the driving seat of my car, when Susan appeared at the door with a see-through dressing gown on and nothing underneath. She just stared at me in the car, and waited. She knew that having seen her I would not now dare drive away.

'Larry is upstairs,' were her words of greeting as if I did not know my way up by automatic control.

My legs had been up those stairs so many times, they would have dragged my body up even if it had made an effort to resist. One of the many reasons I had not removed this persecutor from my list was that Larry himself was a cute little kid and always greeted me with a smile and a kiss. To be honest, I had a fondness for the child. It was not his fault he was always ill, it was just his mother's fault that she simply refused to conform to standard medical practice and bring him in to see me rather than waste my time in visiting. I examined the young lad and found that his mother had been correct in her diagnosis, he had an inflamed eardrum, his usual complaint. I wrote out a prescription, packed my medical bag, and prepared to leave.

'You know your way out,' were the thanks I got for the visit and I duly made my own way down the stairs. At the bottom of the stairs was a door which led to the entrance hall, and the front door to the street was about ten to twelve feet from this door. The downstairs flat was occupied by people whom I did not know and as the yale lock of the door at the bottom of the stairs was fixed in the open position I now did not know what to do. Did Susan want this door to her flat left open or closed? I opened the door, went into the entrance hall, closed the door, then hesitated a few moments. Perhaps Susan wanted the door to her flat locked. I turned back, opened the door again, and was just about to shout up the stairs when I heard a male gruff voice shout out from somewhere upstairs:

'Has that f......g Doctor left yet?'

A female voice, my friend Susan, I would have recognised her voice anywhere, shouted back.

'The f......g shitbag of a doctor has just left!'

I did not wait to hear any more of the conversation, left the door as it was open – and banged the front door behind me. I made sure the occupants of that house knew that someone had just left the premises.

I went straight back to the surgery and to the amazement of my receptionists wrote to the London Executive Council requesting them to remove the family from my medical list. I had just had enough! We still however had a problem, Susan worked for the social services and still came into the surgery with messages. In the circumstances, the surgery staff made certain that I was never allowed to have any contact with her. I have not seen Susan for years and hope that she has left the area, but I do know for a fact all her family have moved from Peckham. Apart from Tom I hope I never see them again.

*   *   *

Mr Derby, a five-foot-three inches scraggly-built chap, had served in Malaya during the war. This country must have been in dire straits in 1941 if it had to find shipping to take this puny individual all that distance to help win the war! Whilst in Malaya he had undergone some tribal marriage with the ugliest woman I have ever seen. He must have been drunk at the time. Although, as I have already stated, he himself was nothing to write home about, he was a handsome creature compared to her. I have been to Malaya (now Malaysia) several times myself and have seen so many pretty girls I can never understand how he got landed with this one.

She must have been about twenty years older than he was! She was pockmarked, four-foot-nothing in height, round like a barrel, round-shouldered, and to cap it all her English was almost nonexistent. He had brought her back to England on demobilisation and my first acquaintance with this family was in 1954, when they registered with me as National Health patients. They were living in Upper Chadwick Road at the time and I believed that this Malayan lady was his only wife. I was wrong!

The first time I learned that Mr Derby might be a bigamist was in June 1954, when he brought in this young, fresh-looking English girl to see me: she was three months pregnant. This girl, was exactly opposite in every physical dimension and appearance to his Malayan wife. She was twenty-seven years old, tall, fair, pretty, upright and slender. The question as I saw it was, what this fair lass could have seen in Mr Derby. It was answered very quickly, this girl was unbelievably simple. Today she would be classed as E S N (educationally subnormal). Although she appeared to understand what one said to her it seemed to take an age for it to sink in and her simplicity projected itself on my first visit to their house. There, I found this English girl slept upstairs in the back bedroom, while the husband with his Malayan wife slept in the front room, downstairs.

One day, I plucked up courage and asked the English wife how she had become pregnant when her husband slept downstairs. She answered me without shame or embarrassment. Whenever her husband – she always referred to Mr Derby as her husband – wanted her for sex he clapped his hands twice, and she would go downstairs to his bed. The Malayan girl – she never called her his wife – would leave the marital bed downstairs and go upstairs to her bed. This arrangement did not appear to her to be at all strange. I made no comment!

I delivered both her children in the upstairs back bedroom in Chadwick Road, and to be fair to the Malayan wife, whatever her facial appearance, she made an excellent nurse. She cared for my young patient beautifully, even the local midwife, Sister Brooks, had nothing but praise at the way she handled the youngster through her confinements. When the children became older, the Malayan wife appeared to take complete charge of their welfare and it was then that I began to have problems with the young Mrs Derby.

Sex, in 1962, was something not often spoken about, especially if one was a young woman and one a young male doctor. This young girl, in her simplicity, used to embarrass me; more to the point, she frightened me. She told me she fancied me and hoped that one day I would give her a baby. When she first told me this I laughed and treated it as a joke. I took the precaution however of never examining her without a chaperone in attendance. She nevertheless developed a fixation about us having a relationship and on one occasion came in to see me to give me a blow-by-blow account of our imaginary sexual encounter. I regarded her talk as so much nonsense, until she came back on two consecutive days, to repeat the same story, in the same explicit way. I had heard of doctors being faced with similar problems of infatuation and the doctor had managed to solve the problem without too much hurt to his family. I was hoping that I would be able to do the same.

On the third day, when she appeared in my surgery as an emergency, repeated her fantasies without complaining of any physical symptoms and began to undress in my consulting room, I became uncomfortable. Uncomfortable is really an understatement. I had never been in this situation before and was at a loss as to how to handle it. I told her to stop undressing and wait a minute. She stopped, looked at me with a smile on her face, and to my amazement began to dress herself. I explained to her that she should see a friend of mine in the Maudsley Hospital who would be interested in her case, and she calmly sat down and watched me in silence while I wrote the referral letter to my friend. While writing the letter my mind was in a turmoil. I wondered how I was going to get her to the Maudsley. I realised that the only way of resolving the situation was to take her to the hospital myself. I therefore sent her back into the waiting room and made her wait until I had finished surgery. I then took her in my car to the emergency clinic.

My luck was in! The doctor she saw in the Maudsley Hospital was the most handsome doctor she had ever seen. She told me so herself on the following day when she brought in his letter advising treatment. His treatment was so successful, she came back to see me on the following day with a blow-by-blow account of a sexual encounter with him! By this time, I was so fed up at seeing this girl every day taking up my time with such nonsense that I telephoned the registrar at the Maudsley Hospital for advice as to how I could get this leech off my back. He told me to send her back to him as an emergency. With a song in my heart, and blessings to the Almighty, I did exactly as he said.

Her behaviour in the hospital must have been very peculiar; the doctor in the emergency clinic telephoned me about an hour afterwards to tell me that my patient was paranoid, needed urgent help, and he was proposing to arrange for her immediate admission. Would I please inform her husband.

Telling her husband that I had arranged for his wife to be admitted to hospital was an experience. I went to see Mr Derby that same evening after he had returned from work to tell him that his wife was a patient in the Maudsley Hospital. The consultant had advised me, I told him, it would be most beneficial for his wife to be an inpatient to enable her to have the best treatment. He broke down as if I had told him she had died. He began to cry. I had to spend some time comforting him. In the end I gave him some tranquillisers to calm him down.

It was then that I heard the true story of the young Mrs Derby and how he had befriended her. She was not his real wife, she was his friend's wife. When his friend had deserted her leaving her friendless and penniless, he had taken her under his wing and pretended to the world that she was his. His friend had married her in 1943, after having had only one blind date with her when she was eighteen years old. His friend, an army mate, had then been posted with Mr Derby to the Far East. On his return to this country in 1946 he found the girl of his dreams, the girl he had proposed to and married after his belly had been filled with beer, was just a dumb blonde with the mentality of a twelve-year-old. He had walked out on her. Mr Derby had befriended her. She was so simple she now honestly believed he was her husband. She had no family.

He had been given to understand by his friend her childhood had been spent in one of Dr Barnado's Homes. At the age of thirty-three she still appeared to have a child's mind and his Malayan wife was probably the best thing that could ever have happened to this poor, simple, child. His real wife was like a mother to her. I passed no opinion on his story. As I now reflect on it, considering the times we were living in immediately after the war he was probably acting in her best interests.

The end result of the story was, the young Mrs Derby was kept in hospital for two months, then allowed home to attend outpatients at fortnightly intervals. The family, after a period, moved to Stockton-on-Tees, and sent me Christmas cards for the first few years. These stopped in 1966, and I have not heard from them since.

* * *

She walked into my consulting room on a busy Thursday evening surgery, *plonked* herself down in the patient's chair, and began to give me a lecture on companionship. Old people she told me are just

70

not respected as they were in her day and her children certainly did not treat her with the same regard as she had treated her patients. I must be honest, I was not too pleased to see her. I had a heavy surgery that evening and being given a lecture on the duties of the young toward their parents was not one of my priorities. I had always cared for my mother and Elizabeth Whitlock, the elderly patient giving me a lecture knew this: obviously something of importance had suddenly occurred to bring this lady into my surgery at a gallop. There was nothing to be done or said on my part, I just sat down firmly in my chair and waited for the narrative to continue and for her to explain the significance of her opening remarks. I did not have long to wait. She had come to see me, she said, to ask whether having sex at her age would be harmful and whether there was any possibility of her becoming pregnant!

I looked at her in astonishment. Nothing she had previously said had prepared me for this statement. Mrs Elizabeth Whitlock was seventy-three years of age. The year was 1982, and as she sat there, it flashed through my mind the good old lady had certainly benefited from the permissive society of the sixties. She had not shown the slightest sign of embarrassment as she had posed her questions. The main point of her coming to see me she continued, was to know whether she should take any precautions when having sex.

I had always regarded Elizabeth Whitlock – she had been my patient for 25 years – as an odd bod, an eccentric, but by no stretch of the imagination as a sex kitten. She was five-foot-nothing in height, and the Almighty had blessed her with a long ugly face which with age had become wrinkly and like parchment. In all the years I had known her she had behaved like a little old lady. Her dress sense matched her appearance and she was, in my opinion, the perfect definition of a *frump*. What puzzled me that Thursday evening and caused me to lose my irritation at the thought of the time wasting in a consultation with the woman was the reason for her present questioning. Who could have possibly stooped to fancy such an unattractive *old bag*?

I had given a death certificate certifying her husband's death some years earlier and had always regarded the pair as a perfectly matched couple. Her husband had been a locksmith, a lovely fellow, always willing to do a good turn. I had known him turn out in the middle of the night to help an unfortunate locked out of his house having lost his keys without even a fleeting sign of annoyance. He had however been a most untidy chap, perhaps fiddling about with greasy locks and not being able to rid his hands and nails from grease had a lot to do with his untidiness. His good lady finding her spouse always greasy and untidy probably thought it made her husband feel more at home by keeping her house untidy and dirty too. To be honest, the chap had been a workaholic, I had never seen him without grease ingrained in his fingers and under his nails. If Elizabeth Whitlock could be called a female *old bag*, his dress sense was such he could have been called a male *old bag*.

Mrs Whitlock, in spite of her failings, had been a good wife and mother, and when the poor chap had fallen ill with complications of his diabetes had nursed him back to health. They had been a happy couple until the Good Lord had trouble with his locks and decided that he needed Mr Whitlock's expertise and called him upstairs. Mr Whitlock had been driving his car home one day when he was forced to brake sharply and he had the misfortune to skid on an oil patch. His car was in a head-on collision with a heavy lorry and he was killed instantly. He had worked with oil all his life so perhaps it was justice oil was the cause of his departure from it.

Mrs Elizabeth Whitlock, a widow of five years standing, was now sitting quite nonchalantly in her doctor's consulting room and asking him whether it was in order for her to have sex! My mind boggled! With tongue in cheek and a good deal of *chutzpah* I asked her who the lucky fellow might be. She answered without hesitation.

'I thought you knew. Everyone else seems to know my business. It's Mr Wheeler.'

'You mean the chap next door to you,' I said.

'Yes. You know him, he has been a patient of yours for years.'

She was not wrong. I did indeed know Mr Wheeler. He and his wife had been patients of mine for almost as long as the Whitlocks. Mrs Wheeler had been a dear lady, crippled with rheumatoid arthritis at a very young age and had suffered her illness with dignity and little complaint. She had died the previous year. She had been a joy to talk to for she had been a very religious woman. She prayed every day, and believed that pain and suffering were penance – God's punishment for past misdeeds. She had suffered her pain stoically in the belief that having served her sentence in this world she would be granted a seat in paradise immediately she entered the next. Her pain and suffering had been at times so severe that I thought if she honestly believed this she must have been some lady of leisure and pleasure before it had been my fortune, or perhaps misfortune, to meet the good lady. I never discussed her youth, or why she held her views with such passion, but we had many discussions on crime, punishment and penance. I could never get her to alter her opinions. She had read up the subject of penance so well that she often bettered me in debate by quoting sections of the *Talmud* where the rabbis endorsed her views. The fact that I disagreed with them she viewed with heresy on my part, even though she knew I regarded myself as religious and God-fearing.

Her rheumatism was a long illness and she was finally confined to a wheelchair. This still did not prevent her from viewing her illness as God's punishment for her past wickedness. Mr Wheeler had been a support to his wife during the whole of her illness and insisted that they spend their once a year holiday in the same boarding house, in Devon, where the landlady welcomed not only them but their wheelchair too. Mr Wheeler would drive down to Devon with the wheelchair strapped to the roof, but just as grease and oil had been the undoing of Mr Whitlock, the undoing of Mrs Wheeler was due to the wheelchair. Mr Wheeler had been pushing his wife down a hill on holiday in Devon when a wheel sheared off the chair and poor Mrs Wheeler fell out. She was taken to hospital where X-rays showed that she had sustained a fractured leg. The fracture was set, she was kept in a hospital bed for four days, suffered a pulmonary embolism, and gained a *seat in paradise* just four days after a minor accident.

Mrs Wheeler was only fifty-nine years old when she died, her husband was two years older, just sixty-one, when Mrs Whitlock questioned me about her relationship with him. It was on the tip of my tongue to ask the lady whether she had gone out of her way to get herself a *toy boy*. There was a twelve year gap in their ages! My brain luckily controlled my tongue. After all, one has to be kind to old ladies. I asked instead whether Elizabeth had enjoyed her neighbour's physical attributes before his wife's death. I was being provocative, playful, but I had trouble: Mrs Whitlock just could not understand what physical attributes were. When I explained what my verbiage meant I thought our doctor and patient relationship would end with the doctor receiving a black eye.

'Certainly not!' were the two words almost screamed at me by the aggrieved lady. The note of disapproval in her voice was a reprimand for my even having had the audacity to think such a thing.

'I felt sorry for Mr Wheeler when his wife died for he seemed so cut up and lonely,' she said.

'I invited him in for dinner one day and he liked my cooking so much that he asked me whether if he paid me for the dinner he could come again. I liked his company so much that I said yes. We agreed that we would have dinner together every Friday night. We shared expenses and as we became such good friends I agreed that I would cook and share a meal with him every evening when he came back from work. After all, his house is so much bigger than mine and it therefore costs so much more to keep warm. The old age pension isn't very much, and it's stupid using two fires and two lots of electricity. By having supper at my place we are saving money. We have over the year become such close friends, when it was cold one night last week, he decided to stay with me and share my bed for warmth. We had earlier shared a bottle of wine watching a naughty film on television, so when in bed we decided to try to be young again. It hurt a bit at first, but it wasn't all that bad and as he enjoyed it so much I am glad that I went through with it. It made him so happy. I have now had second thoughts about our behaviour in case I have become pregnant. He has two grown-up married daughters who have children of their own and it would not be nice if anything happened.'

'You did say become pregnant?' I asked in astonishment.

'Yes.'

I could not believe my ears. A person in this day and age could be so ignorant! She had made her statement so seriously I could not laugh. I could only attribute her nonsense to age, that her mental functions did not apparently match up to her physical ones. Eccentricity had always been her complaint, but I had never considered her to be so stupid as to believe that a person of her mature years would be capable of becoming pregnant even though her partner might be twelve years her junior.

I have in my whole life always treated life as a joke – it is so short – and after listening in silence now returned to my natural behaviour. I managed to send Mrs Whitlock away a very happy woman. I explained to her that her young boyfriend's fears were groundless. Her first name was not *Sarah* who had a baby when ninety years old but *Elizabeth*, and there was no way a lady with this name at her age could ever become pregnant.

If her friend wanted to have sex with her and she was agreeable I advised her how to have painless sex. I also reassured her, if his daughters ever found out about the relationship, they would be delighted to know all their father's requirements were being catered for.

* * *

Some incidents are both funny and tragic, but sometimes the tragic elements can be found to destroy the funny ones.

Mr and Mrs Mason to all appearances were a happily-married couple, until the incident which I am about to relate in 1979 took place. He was fifty-four years old, she was fifty-three, and they had always prior to the crisis appeared at the surgery together. Never at the same time afterwards.

Mr Mason (Richard) looked every bit of his age, indeed, although his actions were those of a forty-year-old lecher, his face was that of a man in his seventies. His face must have been due to the lifestyle he had led prior to becoming my patient and my success in treating him and allowing him to continue his habits. He suffered with his nerves, and attended the surgery very much more often than was good for me and that I would have liked. He was a pain in the neck! He was not one of my original patients but of one of my partners and for some inexplicable reason when my partner was on holiday he attached himself to me. Once he had seen me he recognised an *easy touch* and would not let go. However much I tried to persuade him that I did not specialise in nerve problems and my partner did I was unable to shake the leech off my back. I regarded him as a waster; he and work were deadly enemies. He made it his duty to be away from work all the time. He exaggerated his symptoms and like so many patients with psychological problems complained of ailments which defied anatomical and physiological boundaries.

As he was off work for such long periods with imaginary illnesses my sympathies always tended to rest with his wife, Doris. She was a frail little lady, four-foot-nothing in height, as thin as a rake, and she only weighed five-stone-six ounces – this when fully dressed. She suffered from mitral stenosis (a heart complaint) as a result of having had rheumatic fever as a child, and she told me that as a girl of fourteen she had spent twenty weeks in a hospital bed, sixteen of these had been on complete rest. She had – when confined to bed – not even been allowed to leave her bed to go to the toilet. Her schooling had suffered severely as a result of her illness. She could neither read nor write. Perhaps this was the explanation for her having married such a specimen as Richard Mason. She was breathless even on walking a few yards and her ankles and feet – more often than not – at the end of a day looked like pumpkins. Walking was such a strain, she therefore avoided going out as much as she could.

Richard Mason was Doris's second husband. Her first husband had been a drunken lout, who had made a habit of beating her up in his drunken bouts and the only decent thing he had ever done in his life was to drink himself into an early grave. He had only been forty-three years old when he died but had, before departing this life, managed in three sober periods to impregnate his wife three times. She had benefited from these ministrations with horrific confinements which on each occasion had nearly ended her life. Mrs Mason had two sons and one daughter, but not one of them spoke about their father even after his death with any affection. He had always been too drunk to notice them. Richard had obviously caught Doris on the rebound for he did not drink and was vehemently opposed to its use in any shape or form. Their marriage however – this was not told to me until after the crisis – was not a happy one. Although Richard did not drink he liked to socialise, behave like a *man about town* and loved to go dancing. He was an ugly fellow, with a face like a crab apple, the opposite sex however apparently did not see him in the way I did.

Doris came to see me one day as an emergency, on her own, and this to me was a novel experience: she had always previously been accompanied by her ugly husband. She was so distraught, not only did I fear for her sanity, but her life too. She was not only breathless on the least exertion – she had to stop to take a breath after each step – she also found it difficult to compose herself and stop shaking. Her lips were purple. As she appeared to be unable to speak coherently I examined her heart and finding that it had not suffered any major breakdown was forced to attribute her symptoms as due to stress. I gave her some water to drink. After a few minutes of rest in a chair, sobbing, she quietened down enough to explain why she had come to see me in such a hurry and in such a distressed condition without having gone through the routine of making an appointment.

Her symptoms, she explained, had only appeared following her attendance at an engagement party to which she had been invited the previous evening. One of her daughter's girl friends, a young Scottish lass of twenty-four had got herself engaged and made a party to celebrate the event. Neither Doris nor her daughter had previously met the fiance and Doris's daughter had managed to persuade her mother to come to the engagement party as a special treat. The invitation had only been extended to Doris and her daughter, the fact the invitation had not included Richard had evidently escaped their notice. Doris's daughter had hired a car to take them to the party and bring them back home afterwards. She knew her mother's heart condition would not have allowed her to attend otherwise.

They arrived at the party in excellent spirits and were greeted at the door by the engaged girl's parents. Dad was wearing a kilt and as Doris was wearing a tartan skirt they had engaged in some *repartee* before being taken into the reception hall to be introduced to the happy couple and the other guests. The faces of Doris and her daughter must have been a sight to behold when they were introduced to the couple for whom the party had been organised. The fiance was Mrs Mason's husband – Richard! Doris fainted. After a few glasses full of brandy had been forced through Doris's mouth, she had been packed into a car and sent home. Unfortunately, not enough alcohol had been forced through her resisting lips not to enable her to spend a sleepless night.

To my amazement this event did not break up the Mason's marriage. After the initial shock – Richard actually came home after the party as if nothing out of the ordinary had occurred – the marriage continued, except that Doris now had nerve problems added to her heart condition. Richard, now no longer able to be legally engaged, continued to live in the matrimonial home while still courting his girlfriend and living on social security.

The family eventually moved on to the North Peckham estate. As Doris now found the short walk to my surgery too much for her she changed to a doctor who practised on the estate. Unfortunately, Richard, however much I tried to persuade him to follow his wife and register with her doctor, refused to leave me.

After living on the estate for two years, Richard came to see me one day in a distressed condition. His wife, he told me, had died a few weeks earlier, and his family had now completely deserted him and even refused to speak to him. Even his unmarried stepdaughter, who had lived with them whilst his wife had been alive, had moved. He had no idea where she had gone and she had evidently made sure he would not find out for she had changed her job too.

His loneliness however was evanescent; on the following day he reappeared at my surgery. Could I please give him a supply of his tablets to last for two months as he was leaving me and Peckham to go and live with his girlfriend in Hackney. He needed the tablets as it would take some time to find a suitable doctor there. I did as he asked, I was glad to see the back of the parasite. He has thank heavens never reappeared.

* * *

Elizabeth Shand was a young, ginger-haired, twenty-seven-year-old Scottish lassie, who lived with her husband and young daughter in a basement flat in Lyndhurst Way, in 1957. She was a regular attender at the surgery, sometimes on account of her young daughter's ailments, more often because of her own, and her complaints were always related to her husband's behaviour. Her husband was a much older man, he was twenty years her senior and why she had married a man so much older than herself I never had the courage to ask her. Her husband, according to Elizabeth Shand, did not enjoy normal sex, and she spent a lot of my time describing to me her husband's sexual deviations. Her descriptions of his behaviour were so bizarre, inexperienced and uneducated as I was in sexual deviations, I did not know whether to believe her. Abnormal sexual behaviour was ill-documented in the fifties, was swept under the carpet, the pretence was it never existed. If it never existed it had to be assumed it did not happen, it was therefore the product of a fertile mind. Vivid imagination because of the age gap I considered to be the problem in this case. But as my experience of treatment in this field was nil, the only help I was able to give was to sit and listen and act as a safety valve.

The fact that the couple had a daughter may have been a cementing factor in their relationship until one evening, when the girl was three years old, Mr Shand knocked at my surgery door at nine-thirty to enquire as to whether I had called to see his daughter that day. He explained he was a gas fitter and had had an emergency call out just as he was due to return home which had taken him longer to deal with than he had anticipated. He had only just arrived home. This is why he had come to see me so late in the evening. My mind was in turmoil at his appearance. I stammered that I had not thought it necessary to see his daughter that day. His daughter had not appeared ill enough when I had last seen her to require a daily visit. After all, I said with more conviction, she only had tonsillitis and I had seen her the previous day. I had seen her when she had been very much worse and she had always managed to get better in a couple of days.

'You shouldn't worry so much. If she is no better in the morning, I will come and see her again.'

He looked at me speechless for a second then burst into tears. I was thunderstruck! I had evidently completely misdiagnosed the poor girl. Something dreadful had obviously happened to cause her father to break down in such a fashion. I now did not know what to say or do. I just grabbed an overcoat, put an arm around the fellow's shoulders and walked home with him. Of one thing I was certain, the couple needed help. As we walked, I wondered how I could have missed a diagnosis which had been so obvious as to cause a tragedy of this magnitude. By the time we had reached the house I was numb and dumb. I remember quite distinctly, neither of us had spoken a word as we walked into Upper Chadwick Road, then crossed the road into Lyndhurst Way, and into the Shand home.

He did not bother to open the door to his flat – the door was open. I blinked. I could not believe my eyes! The electric light bulb – minus shade – in the living room was on, but this was the only thing which appeared at first glance to be present in the whole flat. The flat was empty! It was unbelievable! Not only had the flat been deserted by his wife and daughter it had been stripped bare of all furniture and fittings. The only thing which had been left was the sink with the cold water tap: even the hot tap with the Ascot gas water heater had been removed.

My surprise must almost have been as great as his. I had visited the flat on the previous day and at no time had Mrs Shand intimated to me in any conceivable way that she had any intention of no longer requiring my services. Indeed, as I had left, I had told her that should her daughter not respond to treatment in a couple of days she should send for me again. She had agreed to do so. My treatment had obviously worked wonders in that it had allowed mother to spirit the couple away after only one day.

I never found out why Mrs Shand chose that particular moment in time to move away lock stock and barrel: or the way she had contrived to move so completely without her husband even being remotely aware of the fact. The neighbours had been told by Mrs Shand when the removal van was at the door that she was having some old furniture removed and replaced with new. They had given the matter no further attention until Mr Shand's return and surprise. The only thing which they had thought strange at the time was that the van had come from Folkestone. What business was it of theirs however to worry about where the Shands decided to buy their new furniture!

I have never seen Mrs Elizabeth Shand since the day she did her disappearing act, she and her daughter changed doctors within weeks of the move, but her husband remained a patient of mine until the day of his death. On that fateful night, I drove him to his sister's house in Shawbury Road, East Dulwich, and he remained living with her for the rest of his life – over thirty years. He told me on many occasions that he had tried to trace his wife, but without success. He never bothered to obtain a divorce as he had no intention of getting married again, but after twenty-five years an amazing thing happened. He had by this time been retired for some years with severe heart trouble which had prevented him from even doing part-time work: his financial state therefore was a precarious one.

One evening, when I was doing a normal evening surgery, I was interrupted while examining a patient by one of my receptionists to ask whether I would accept an emergency call from a Miss Shand. At the time I did not relate the call to one of my patients but agreed to speak to the young lady. Imagine my surprise therefore when I heard the voice on the phone identify herself to be the Miss Shand whom I had last seen twenty-five years earlier: she had then been a child of three. She had telephoned to ask me whether her father was still a patient of mine, and if the answer was yes, could I please give her his address.

Her story was, she had not seen her father since her mother had left Peckham and as they had never been in contact she had no idea where he was living. Indeed, she did not know whether the old chap was still alive as she had been told that her father had been twenty years older than her mother. She had never bothered to find out anything about him until she herself had fallen in love and decided to get married. She now wanted to invite her father, if still alive, to her wedding, to give her away. It was only when she had pestered her mother to know something of her parentage that she had been told that she had no idea where her father was or even whether he was still alive. The only person who might possibly know anything of his whereabouts was a Doctor Crown in Peckham, but she did not know whether the fellow was still in practice. When she had telephoned me she did not even know whether I was the same Dr Crown who had been her mother's doctor so many years ago.

I was overjoyed at hearing her request and had no hesitation whatsoever in giving her father's address to her. He had told me so many times that if God was good to him he would see his daughter again before he died. God was indeed good to him. She went to see him and he was so overcome with emotion he passed out. His sister sent for me as she thought he had suffered a heart attack. He had not: his emotion had become so overpowering he had hyperventilated and collapsed as a result. When he recovered, I was delighted to find out that he was able to tell me his daughter was very comfortable financially and was going to make it her duty to provide him with the financial support which he so desperately needed. He was now actually going to have a little comfort in his old age.

I never found out what had happened to make his wife leave him in such a hurry and with such a *clear out*. I never myself ever met the daughter to ask what her mother had told her, and I did not want to ask Mr Shand and open up wounds which had long remained dormant by asking him.

He died four years after his daughter's reappearance – a very happy man.

*　　*　　*

John Taylor and Francine Corby had been brought up together, their parents had lived next door to each other in Denman Road, in the forties. They were the same age and having been born within six months of each other became very close friends. They went to Lyndhurst School together, were in the same class, and it was therefore no surprise when Francine married Ronald Corby that Ronald and John should become friends too. The friendship was perhaps inevitable, Ronald and John worked as mechanics in the same garage. Since the total staff of this repair shop was three, one of whom was the boss, the two men were in each other's company all day long: the fact that Francine was married to Ronald just cemented the friendship. John lived some distance away from his work and as Ronald and Francine lived just a stone's throw away, more often than not, he spent his lunch time at their home.

When John, at the ripe old age of twenty-nine, decided to get married to Melanie, a freckled-faced, nineteen-year-old Yorkshire lass, it was the most natural thing in the world that he should ask Ronald to be his best man. The wives continued the friendship, the families became inseparable and they could be said to live in each other's houses. They even went away on holiday together. I knew both families well as their parents and most of their families were patients of mine. I also had the privilege of delivering the Corby and Taylor children into the world.

The Corbys had four children, three were Ronald's, they looked like him, behaved like him, and had the same facial characteristics. Although not explicitly told so, the fourth child was almost certainly John's. All the children were girls, but even as a girl, the fourth could be said to have been John's *spitting image*. Not only did she look like him, she was fair like John, not with the Mediterranean appearance of Ronald and her three sisters. The reason for my supposition that the fourth girl was John's will be obvious from my story.

Francine had only been married for two years before she came in to see me complaining of her husband's lack of interest in sex. Not only was he now not interested in sex, nothing appeared to interest him. In her denunciation of his sexual behaviour she was however quite explicit.

'I don't know what's come over him, he was so much better at it before we got married!'

As the years went by her complaints instead of being resolved became more numerous and caustic. She came in one day for some nerve pills, and wasted my time by elucidating her problems with Ronald in detail. All he was interested in now she told me was beer, television and cigarettes.

He came home from work every night with a bellyful of beer, slopped his supper down like a pig, put on his slippers, sank down in an armchair in front of the television and fell asleep. It would not be so bad if he didn't snore so loudly, his loud snoring stopped her from enjoying the television. Although people regarded him as a home-loving man they were only partially right. He did not regard home as a living place, it was just a place where a chap could put his head down and drop off to sleep. He had, from the day the first child had been born, never been any help with the children. What made matters worse, he never realised he had to help. She could not remember when he had last offered to take her out! He was completely devoid of ambition! She could not recollect why she had fancied such a *cabbage!* He had no hobbies, unless drinking to excess could be called a hobby. When she had been courted he had been a tall, good-looking, athletic, young man; as the years had gone by he had changed – unfortunately for the worse. He had become more and more like a *fat slob*. Were it not for the fact that the children were small and she needed a roof over her head she would have left her good-for-nothing husband ages ago.

It is strange really, how fate often plays funny tricks with people's lives. Francine, who constantly complained of her husband's idleness found in the end idleness forced upon him.

He was forty years old, it was his birthday, he had probably imbibed too much 'hop mixture' at lunch time, when he had a serious accident at work. He fell off the top of a hoist and sustained a fractured femur, with compound fractures of tibia and fibula. Unfortunately, after the operation to plate his fracture he suffered a pulmonary embolism and was on the critical list in the hospital acute care unit for some weeks. He recovered, and when due to be sent home had a heart attack. Altogether, his inpatient stay in hospital lasted for thirty-two weeks. When I heard from Francine that he was due to come home we celebrated, but our pleasure was short-lived. This time, on the day he was due to be released, he had an attack of bronchopneumonia; this meant a further period of hospitalisation. As if he had not been punished enough, when he recovered from his bronchopneumonia he suffered a stroke. When he finally arrived home he was a chronic respiratory cripple, a hemiplegic, and was only able to get about with the aid of crutches.

At the age of forty-one, Ronald now looked like a man in his eighties. He had, as I have already described, never been an active person. Now, looking like an old man, he had no chance except to behave like one too. John in comparison looked forty years younger than his friend and whatever his motives may have been at the time he behaved like a gentleman. He became the best friend anyone could have had. He fetched and carried. He even lent them money to tide them over difficult periods when they were short of ready cash. It is an irony of life, sick people usually require more money to cope with day-to-day problems and are inevitably forced by circumstances to manage with less.

With Ronald completely out of action both physically and sexually John – after waiting for what he must have thought to be the requisite period of time – told Francine that he had always been in love with her. She, not Melanie, was the girl whom he should really have married. It had been unfortunate he had lacked the courage to ask her. Francine was extremely flattered. His feelings had intensified he told her as a result of the care and attention which she had shown to her sick husband. He knew that

Ronald, although still his friend, had never given her much of a life even when he had been fit and well. He had now fallen hopelessly in love with her and as he could not live without her suggested they become lovers. Francine admitted to me she had been rather startled at first by John's proposal. She thought however no harm would be done by accepting his proposition. At no time did she ever intend to leave her sick husband, she had only acquiesced as a *bit of a giggle.*

The minute she agreed to become his lover he immediately booked a room in a hotel in Dulwich for a *lovemaking.* The time was just one day after his proposal and her acceptance. He had obviously had it all prearranged as it was for 8.00 o'clock on Wednesday evening. And for the following nine years they met on the same evening, in the same room, for a repeat performance. She had no idea how he had made the original booking, but as they were provided with the same room, at the same time, every week, for the same purpose, for one hour, John must have taken an option on it! The one thing she admitted however was whatever his faults John made a superb lover.

Both John and Francine had ready-made excuses to their respective spouses for their absences. John's excuse was that he was now having to do overtime to make up the schedule of work required by the garage to cover Ronald's absence. The extra money he earned made it easier to finance their holidays which they took regularly. Francine's excuse was that she was tied to the house all week and needed a break. What better way to spend it than playing bingo. It only cost a few bob, in any event she was only away a couple of hours. I have already stated this *scenario* continued for nine years and I must be honest, I became fed up to the back teeth with the time-wasting this entanglement caused me as I listened to the stories of both parties.

Francine, in the sexually-starved relationship with her husband, fantasized that John was madly in love with her and not just for the sexual pleasure of her body. He had told her he was in love with her and could not live without her, why should she not want to believe him? Even when Ronald had been fit she had felt badly used and I had been the safety valve as a forced listener to her constant carping of her husband's lovemaking technique. Her husband believed lovemaking consisted of penetration, ejaculation, withdrawal and sleep. There was no foreplay, no afterplay, indeed no play at all – she just bore his children. She had reached the stage by the time Ronald had his accident of making every excuse under the sun to avoid having sex. The accident had been a godsend.

Now she was enjoying sex again, even if it was for only one hour-a-week, I once again became a forced listener, this time to the stories of her *happy hour.* There was one hiccough in the affair. After it had lasted three years Francine, now thirty-eight years old, presented herself at my surgery with what she thought to be a fibroid in her womb. Her friend had suffered similar symptoms, had been diagnosed by her doctor as having a uterine fibroid and she was going to have it removed. I was able after examining Francine to put her mind at rest. She did not have a fibroid. She had a four-month's pregnancy instead. How she came to explain her pregnancy to her invalid husband I have never had the courage to ask, but I did give her full marks for bravery. Never once did she suggest to me that she have the pregnancy terminated. She went to term and presented her husband with a blonde daughter. Her husband, Ronald, in his conversation with me afterwards never once intimated to me that the baby might not be his. Therefore, one assumes, there must have been either some sexual relationship with Francine in spite of his disability, or he thought it wise not to probe too deeply into his wife's affairs.

When Francine realised that she was pregnant she told John of her predicament. Although they both knew he was the cause of her pregnancy, John told her there was no way he could leave his wife at that particular time. His own children were small, they needed him, and indeed, he could not do such a thing while Ronald was alive. He was after all her husband's best friend! Besides, it would be most ungentlemanly to treat a chap who was so seriously ill in this fashion. To take Francine away while Ronald was still alive would be cruelty of the worst kind. It would almost certainly kill the poor chap and John would not be able to live with himself.

This affair in itself would have been of little interest to me as many of my patients were probably having affairs. But apart from the time-consuming, it presented me with problems. I had been the family doctor to both families since I had opened my practice in Peckham and my problem was in finding answers to Melanie when she came to complain of her husband's lack of interest in sex.

Melanie, was a young woman in her late twenties, blonde, tall, attractive, with a nice figure. She was always beautifully turned out, she was far better looking than Francine, but Francine must have been much better in bed for John to have preferred her. To complicate matters, Francine and Melanie could be described as best friends. They are still friends, but my problem at that time was, Francine used to enthuse to me over her lover's performance in bed. Why she had to tell me I just don't know, except to guess she needed someone to listen to her needs and assuage her feeling of guilt of how she was behaving to her best friend.

Melanie, to her credit, always brought John with her when she came to complain of her husband's lack of sex drive. In front of him she told me that he now appeared to have no interest in sex at all. She could not understand what had happened to him. She attributed it to his work schedule. He had been fine before he had started to work extra hours. He now came home tired and exhausted after a day's work and as his lack of interest had only occurred since Ronald's return from hospital it was obviously due to the extra work he was having to do as a result of Ronald's absence.

On Wednesday evenings, after doing overtime, he did not come home until eleven o'clock at night! He was then so exhausted he often fell asleep in the middle of eating his supper. There must be something I could prescribe to help a young man improve his performance. To prevent a break-up of the marriage I constantly prescribed aphrodisiacs to help John, but they never helped. How could they? If aphrodisiacs helped with problems such as John's there would be a mountain of prescriptions for them.

What infuriated me was John's behaviour as he sat in my consulting room listening to his wife's complaints. He just sat there motionless, whilst she complained that both he and I were failures. He was a failure in that he now had no interest in her as a lover. I was a failure in that I did not appear to be able to cure him and from the way he was being treated it did not appear that he ever would be! There were many times when I had to press my tongue into my cheek to prevent me saying, *'My treatment is excellent, Francine has no complaints!'* John, who did not know that Francine confided in me, just sat in his chair like a scalded-cat, not saying a word, whilst his wife berated me at my lack of success. Staring into space like a brainless-twit, he did not show the slightest embarrassment. I suppose he did not think he had to be embarrassed, he was performing alright! I also wished I could have said to him,

'You manage alright with Francine, why can't you save a bit for your wife?'

In 1979, Ronald suffered a massive heart attack, his fourth, but on this occasion I was too late: he died before I got to him. Now there was a fly in the ointment! John had constantly told Francine that if Ronald died he would leave his wife and make a new life with her. Francine had listened to him but had never expected him to do so. Although she had never minded cheating on Melanie, she had still regarded herself as her best friend. When John, thinking Francine would pressurise him to leave told her that he now intended to give up their Wednesday evenings, she was devastated.

John came to his friend's funeral, spoke a few words to his ditched mistress, then did not get in touch with her for months. Melanie still remained her friend, but things were not the same. John now made every excuse for not going to see her even when accompanied by his wife. Both John and Melanie had been her best friends, now Melanie alone remained. Francine would have been quite happy for their Wednesday meetings to continue after Ronald's death as if nothing had happened. John however had got cold feet. She had never expected to be treated as a leper by her former lover! She would have thought that after all the years they had been lovers he would have known better than suspect her of being a person who would have wanted to break up her friend's marriage. *She now not only felt used, but abused!*

After a period of mourning at the loss of a lover whom she felt had betrayed her, Francine joined a lonely hearts club. A young-looking grandmother, she has found many lonely hearts who have been prepared to share her mourning, her morning, and her bed. I last saw her a couple of months ago and when I asked her how she was coping she told me that she would be travelling abroad again. She had met a fellow in the club who liked to travel to tropical islands. Liking his warmth and that of the islands which they visited she was now on her third trip there.

I am now able to write this story of the entanglement without any feeling of betrayal. John dropped dead some time ago while on holiday with his wife and family. He had been changing some gas cylinders at their caravan when he complained of chest pain. Before the family had even had time to send for assistance John was already wending his way to join Ronald. I attended his funeral without him ever having known that I knew of his conduct and behaviour towards Francine. Francine and Melanie are still friends: their families always spend their Christmases together.

4

Meshuga

In the seventies, before our group took Dr Lai
Cheng Wong, a lady doctor, as a partner, Amelia
worked for the practice for some time as a part-time
assistant. When Amelia was interviewed for the post
it was pointed out to her that she would be required
to do home visits if necessary, but what she had
forgotten to inform me she had no car! More to the
point, she had no intention of ever getting one. The
first time she was given a home visit to do was the
first time I found out this transport deficiency. She
spent four-and-half hours doing the visit, and it was
only in Meeting House Lane, within easy walking
distance of the surgery. On reflection, perhaps she
was not so eccentric as she made out; taking so long
to do one home visit and having no car prevented
the practice from using her for this purpose.

Amelia was short, under five-foot, always dressed
like a pathetic old lady, and when she spoke there
was no one who could not recognise her guttural
German-English accent. On the days when she did
an evening surgery she would appear in Peckham in
the early afternoon and sit in the park in Holly
Grove, near the toilets. When she first began to

work for us she would come at midday, sit in reception driving the staff mad, and I was forced to tell her not to come until the time for her surgery actually commenced. This made her come to Peckham an hour later, in the early afternoon. She would then eat her lunch in the shrubbery in Holly Grove and tell anyone who happened to recognise her and was prepared to listen it was *THAT* Dr Crown who forced her to be in the situation where she had to eat her lunch next to the toilets.

She was such a quaint creature. She found it difficult to come to terms with my sense of humour and finding her such an easy target I must admit I behaved atrociously. Her constant moan to me that the income tax people would not leave her alone and were bent on persecuting her caused me to remark one afternoon that I had seen an income tax man waiting for her on the corner of her road. With as straight a face as I could muster, I told her that when I had commenced my visits at eleven-thirty that morning I had seen the chap at the corner of her road. Lo and behold, he was still there when I had passed at three o'clock in the afternoon. The fact that she lived in Hammersmith, there was no possible way I could have been within ten miles of her home escaped her notice. None of us is particularly fond of the taxman, but she had an income tax persecution complex. The very mention of the term made her lose all reason. On hearing my fictitious story she became hysterical and began to scream.

'Mein gott! Vere did they get mein address from? I can't do surgery. I must go home at vunce.'

I spent the next ten minutes of my valuable time persuading her that my remarks were jokes and she had nothing to worry about. My concern at the time was that she would indeed leave to go home and I would have *shot myself in the foot.* I would not only have my own patients to see but hers too. It would have served me right!

No one ever saw her without the same old beret firmly perched on her head. She failed to realise this made her appear older than she really was. She claimed at the interview that she was fifty years old. She looked seventy! As she had a son in his twenties the beret added twenty years to her appearance and to be honest it indeed looked as if it was twenty years old! Interestingly, the beret was a subject of conversation to all the patients who ever had to see her, it gave the appearance of having been made to fit her scalp and cemented on to it. This item of clothing caused patients to ask the staff whether the lady doctor had any hair.

Amelia came to us as a locum after a period of service in one of the central African republics, but as she was so vague on the subject and reluctant to speak about it, it appeared hurtful to press her for details. The only statement I ever heard her to make on the subject was, she had at one time been married to an engineer who worked in the Central African Republic. She never told us what happened to him, whether he was alive or dead, or whether she was separated or divorced. Whatever her previous life had been one thing was obvious, she had been starved of affection. This was apparent many times in the surgery when she went emotionally over the top for some small kindness which she received from a member of the staff.

Peckham has never been the easiest place for receptionists to work in and one afternoon – after a very busy and frustrating morning, after the patients had given the staff a particularly gruelling time – I had a sudden urge to buy the overworked girls some chocolates. I went to the local confectioners and appeared a few minutes later in reception with a bag of Mars bars. Seeing Amelia in the room there was no way I was going to leave her out and I considered it the most natural thing in the world to offer her one. What I had not anticipated was her reaction. She grabbed hold of me, wrapped herself around me, smothered me with kisses, became so affectionate that I retreated in confusion. Had I remained, I am sure the girls would have choked in trying to contain their hysterical laughter and eat a Mars bar at one and the same time.

Amelia was Jewish and pretended to keep a *kosher* home. Why she repeatedly had to tell everyone this I could never fathom out. She never invited me for a meal in her home, nor if she had would I have accepted her invitation. It was not that I disliked her, she was such an odd bod. I would not have been surprised if she had served up cat food! Her obsession of telling everyone that she kept *kosher* almost equalled her obsession about the tax man. When I once mentioned in reception Amelia claimed only to eat *kosher*, I was met with the look of one stoney-faced receptionist who remarked,

'Bloody liar! I have just had a hamburger with her in McDonalds.'

She came to me one day and asked for a holiday so that she could make funeral arrangements for herself in Israel. I could not refuse. She had worked in the practice long enough to entitle her for some leave. It was after this holiday I realised Amelia was not just an eccentric, she had mental problems too. She had not personally, as I thought, gone to Israel, but arranged with go-knows-who to have her body dropped over that country – 'unwrapped'! She told the staff this in all seriousness and believed every word she said.

The police telephoned one evening whilst I was in the surgery and Amelia was away ill, enquiring whether we employed a lady doctor by the name of Amelia. They had gone to her home – they would not tell me why – and in their search had found a pad of blank prescriptions with the name and address of our surgery stamped on them. It was their belief that these had been stolen from us and wanted to check whether we had reported the loss. When I told the policewoman on the phone that we did indeed employ a lady by the name of Amelia as a part-time assistant, I could sense even over the phone a feeling of disbelief. There was stunned silence for a few seconds. The voice then said,

'have you ever been here doctor?'

'No!' was my reply. 'Well, you would have the shock of your life doctor!' was the answer on the phone.

I learned that she shared a room with her son and there was a curtain in the middle of the room partitioning it into two halves. He was never allowed to cross the border into her half of the room and she had constant quarrels with her son when he violated her territory.

We had employed her so that the practice could have the benefit of a lady doctor, but it cost us dearly, both socially and financially. On the one and only occasion she was asked to do a cervical smear the room afterwards looked as if it had been the scene of a violent struggle. The couch blankets were strewn all over the floor. The pillow was under the sink. The heavy-swivel chair was overturned, and papers and forms littered the desk. The final result was, Amelia had not bothered to fix the slide! The patient had to be recalled to have the smear repeated. This time however not by Amelia. She had spent her whole surgery doing this one failed smear! Her employment by the practice was certainly not cost effective!

Patients who consulted her would often be in her surgery for ages and come out as if hypnotised. I shall never forget one chap having just consulted her, walking out of her consulting room with his eyes glazed, in sheer disbelief. I knew the man well, he had seen me on numerous occasions, and as he passed me in the corridor on his way out I passed some jocular remark. He walked like a *zombie*, looked neither to his right nor his left. He ignored me completely. He went out of the surgery repeating to himself,

'*she's mad, she's mad*'. I did not try to follow him to ask him why he thought this. It was plain for all to see that he was in a state of shock. I went to Amelia and asked her what she had said to the chap and she then went into great detail as to how one should instruct patients to take their medication.

'You haf to tell the patients vot to do with the medicine. Patients are funny people! They never follow vot you say to them. Dis patient had piles you seeee. He did not look too bright, so I told him not to make a mistake and put the suppository in his ear, you seee!'

Much to our relief, she told us one day that she would be leaving the practice as she was moving to another town. We said how sorry we would be to lose her, at the same time thanking God for answering our prayers.

* * *

Mr Ernest Hopwood came in to see me on a cold winter night in January 1971, for the first time. I knew that I had never seen him before, I could never have forgotten a man with such an appearance! He had a scar the whole length of his face, a scar on his neck, and some one-sided hair loss on his skull which gave his face a lopsided appearance. He could have come straight from a horror-movie film set and at first glance it gave me the creeps just to look at him. It is strange really, although I have seen hundreds of deformities in my long experience, the only reason I can give for my feeling of unease when looking at this chap was that I knew nothing about him and the way he looked at me. I had been presented with a blank continuation card by the receptionist. There were no medical records available and his attitude as he planted himself in my consulting room chair made me feel uncomfortable.

'I would like a hundred phenobarbitone and a hundred epanutin' he said – before he had even seated himself, before he had even passed the time of day. He then told me he had not wanted to waste my time and had asked for his prescription at the reception desk but had been refused. The receptionists had rightly told him that for a first visit and a request for a prescription he had to be seen by a doctor. I took a good look at the chap and it was obvious from the scarring on his face that he had been in some sort of accident.

'What do you want phenobarbitone and epanutin for?' I asked.

'For my fits,' was the answer.

'What is the reason for you to have fits?' I asked.

He concentrated on my face for a minute or two without speaking, then broke out in a sickly grin. He furrowed his brow, this appeared to pronounce his facial deformity. I do not think for one moment this was meant to intimidate me, it was just giving him time to think. I was only doing my duty, it would have been medically remiss for me to have given him a prescription for such powerful anticonvulsants without questioning the reason for their necessity. As we continued to stare one another out, he began to tell me the reason of his necessity for the anticonvulsants.

He told me that a doctor had certified him as suffering from post-traumatic epilepsy as a result of an accident which he had suffered five years previously. He had been prescribed anticonvulsants and if he did not have the tablets he had fits. He had run out of them that very morning and as he had just moved into Camberwell Grove he had now come to register and get a prescription. More by medical training than casual observation one knows whether a patient is telling the truth or trying it on, in this case I had no doubt he was telling the truth. As I listened, I knew from his facial expressions and the way he fashioned his sentences the accident had certainly left him with some brain damage.

He had been riding his motorbike in one of the southern coastal towns in 1967, when he had had an accident and been knocked unconscious. He had no recollection of the accident, he only remembered what he had been told. It was obviously not his fault that the lorry he had been overtaking had decided to turn right at the precise moment he was passing it! When I asked him whether the lorry was signalling and indicating its intention to do so he did not appear to comprehend my statement. He had been taken to hospital by ambulance, but could not remember the name of the hospital, the name of any doctor there, or even the name of the town in which the hospital was situated. The accident had certainly affected his memory! He could not even tell me how long his stay in hospital had been.

His first recollection of events was waking up naked, freezing cold, in a massive room, with a sheet over him.

'Do you know doc?' he continued,

'I was not even in a proper bed, just a metal trolley. What a way to treat a patient who has had an accident! What a place to put a chap in! Do you know there were no other patients in this room, just a few empty trolleys? There was this big fridge stuck against the wall. You have never seen such a big fridge in your whole life. It was huge! Do you know it went from one wall to the other? What they wanted such a big fridge for – God only knows. When I sat up and looked around, all I could see was this little old *geezer* walking about and not taking a blind bit of notice.'

His monotonous description of his surroundings and his lack of the later understanding of his predicament rather shook me. There was now no doubt in my mind the accident had seriously affected his brain. He had given me a perfect description of a hospital mortuary.

My mind shot back to 1948, when I had been the casualty officer and orthopaedic houseman, in the Victoria Hospital, Blackpool. This was before the National Health Service, and the resident doctors had to do their own postmortem examinations. We were always run off our feet and to find time to do an examination was always a difficult task. I remember the coroner one day asking for one to be done as an emergency and although the patient who had died had not been one of mine I had been delegated to do the job. The only free time I could find was at one o'clock in the morning and as the report had to be on the coroner's desk by eleven that morning I went down to do the postmortem examination as instructed.

The mortuary was not in the hospital building itself but in the grounds, in a kind of a prefabricated building, next to the tuberculosis ward. The mortuary and tuberculosis ward were probably part of the same structure – my memory fails me here. This building was separated from Stanley Park by a low hedge and was at the summit of a long lawn which swept down to the main part of the park itself. The building therefore was at a higher level than the park, and the wind from the sea used to sweep across the park and howl in the mortuary. The doctors were used to this, no one paid any attention.

I went to the mortuary at 1.30 that morning, opened the door, and noticed to my left, the little chapel which was part of the mortuary housed a coffin raised on a plinth. The coffin and plinth were covered with black velvet drapes which extended to the floor. There was a tall candle, alight, at each corner of the coffin, and a couple of wreaths on top of the coffin. This particular phenomenon did not worry me too much as I had been in this creepy situation before. It was quite common to go into the mortuary and find a coffin with drapes on it.

I went into the postmortem room to the right of the chapel, took out *my body* from the fridge, put it on a metal trolley, and wheeled it into the middle of the room. I deposited it on the slab ready for dissection. I put on my rubber gloves. With a scalpel in my hand ready to make an incision I was stopped by a pleading voice.

'Oh! Please don't!'

The light in the mortuary was not the brightest and I had been working nonstop since four the previous morning. The lighted candles in the next room which could easily be seen from where I stood did not help the situation. Tiredness I thought could play some funny tricks. I closed my eyes, took a deep breath, opened my eyes again and prepared to carry on. I thought my imagination had got the better of me. Once again, with the scalpel in my hand ready to make an incision, the pleading voice rang out,

'Oh, no! Please don't! Oh no!'

I broke out in a sweat and decided to search the room. I opened every drawer of the fridge to make sure the bodies were really dead bodies. They were! I went into the chapel and put my ear to the coffin. No sound emanated from it. The only sounds in the chapel were the howling from the wind outside and some crackling from the candles. The pleading voice now pierced the darkness again and sounded more desperate.

'Oh! No! For heaven's sake, please don't!'

I cracked! I took off my gloves, left the body on the slab, and ran into the main hospital building. I chased along the corridor like a man possessed, took the stairs up to the doctors common room three at a time, and collapsed into a chair. After a very brief respite, I poured myself out a large gin. I was lucky that night, there were two doctors in the room playing cards, but they had only given me a momentary glance as I had burst into the room. One of them then turned to me and said,

'you look as if you have seen a ghost;' as he continued to survey the cards in his hand. I poured myself another glass of gin which I downed in one gulp.

'You should lay off that stuff, it will be the death

of you!' he continued. 'What's the matter? Has she just done the dirty on you and told you she's pregnant?'

As the gin began to have its effect and I became calmer, I hesitantly began to explain the reason for my sudden attack of nerves. They now put down their cards and began to listen intently.

'Do you know?' one of them said,

'I had to stop doing a postmortem one night and leave it until the morning. I heard moaning in the mortuary and it gave me the creeps. Let's go and have a look.'

We all took torches. Although we found the mortuary full of bodies, we found none in a position to make any noise or make a complaint. We searched the mortuary so thoroughly we were certain in no way could it have been a haven for the cause of our disturbances. We then went outside and with our powerful torches searched the hedges which acted as a boundary to the mortuary. We suddenly heard a commotion in the park on the other side of the hedge as our torches swept along. Two angry voices, one male, and one high pitched female screamed out;

'can't you mind your own bloody business!'

We extinguished our torches spontaneously as if by a magic command. We felt better. We now had the explanation for the noises which prevented our night work.

To return to my story of my patient who had an accident in 1971, Ernest Hopwood had recovered consciousness in the morgue! He had no idea of the implication of his next statement.

'You should have seen the face of the little old geezer wandering about the room when I asked him where I was. The silly old fool had been sweeping the floor. He hadn't taken a blind bit of notice of me. It was bloody cold down there, I can tell you. All the bloke did when I sat up and asked him where I was, was to run away. He was no bloody help at all. I was starkers, lying on this metal table, freezing bloody cold, and he didn't even bring me a blanket.'

Ernest showed no emotion at all as he told me the story. He was just telling me the history of his accident and there was no doubt in my mind he was telling me the truth. He had come to me not for help or advice, just to get a repeat of his tablets. I asked him no further questions, but gave him his prescription for phenobarbitone tablets and epanutin capsules and he left. He returned regularly for repeat prescriptions for five more years then left the area and transferred to another practice. I do not know what has become of him.

His medical reports which arrived from the hospital after he had been a patient of mine for some months bore out his story with little variation. He had been involved in an accident when his motorcycle had been crushed by a lorry and he had been brought into the hospital, unconscious. He did not regain consciousness, and for some reason not disclosed in his records he was pronounced dead. There were no details in the report of how long he had been unconscious or what treatment he had received.

Ernest's records had been sent to me from his

previous doctor via the Surrey Executive Council and I had no way of knowing whether more detailed reports had previously been sent then purposely either lost or extracted. The report in my possession simply stated that he had been transferred from the ward to the mortuary where the cold had obviously stimulated him and he had revived. The notes were sketchy, just statements of fact, and I had the impression from this report whoever had written it had given a good deal of thought before its composition. The writer had made it his duty not to give too much detail in case there was intensive investigation, perhaps litigation.

After my experience in the mortuary in Blackpool it was fortunate for my patient that the attendant was able to summon help and did not die of fright on the spot. Perhaps, if the attendant is a drinker, he will have many a drink bought for him when he accounts how, like Elisha the prophet, he brought a person back from the dead.

*   *   *

I was about to commence consultations in my surgery at 5 pm, on a dark Monday evening, in January 1972, when I had an urgent message from Miss Dooley, the psychiatric social worker. I knew Miss Dooley well. When she asked me to come urgently to see one of my patients who had gone berserk I knew that I had to leave my surgery immediately and do her bidding.

This patient, James Marlow, a bachelor, aged

thirty-five years, with a long history of mental illness, lived in an upstairs flat in Melbourne Grove, near Dulwich Hospital. Miss Dooley, had called on a routine visit just to see how James was coping with life. He was a schizophrenic: as he had not kept his routine hospital appointments she had called to ask the reasons why, and she had been confronted by James at the entrance of his flat with an axe in his hand. Not only was the axe threatening, his demeanour was too: having decided that discretion was better than valour she had called the police.

The messages which I had received from my receptionists with the request for the visit were, James, armed with an axe, was standing at the top of the stairs of his upstairs flat and was not prepared to allow anyone to enter. Miss Dooley had called the police for help but they – on being informed James had a mental history – had refused to go up the stairs and confront him. The sergeant in charge had told Miss Dooley that before the police were prepared to do anything James's GP had to see him. Miss Dooley, although she knew I was about to commence my evening surgery had been given no option but to send for me.

I felt sorry for the poor lass. I liked her a lot, she had never troubled me except in an emergency; this obviously had to be one of those occasions. Fortunately, my waiting room only had two patients in it at the time and I told them that I had been called out to do an emergency visit. I would be back as soon as I could and advised them to read the magazines in the waiting room as I would be testing them on the contents when I returned!

My first recollection on arriving at the scene was that of an Austin Mini parked in the road outside the front door, weighed down by the weight of four police officers sitting inside it. Their massiveness filled the car. The car sides appeared to have bulged to meet the requirements of the occupants, and the chassis of this poor little car almost touched the ground. The police had certainly sent the heavy mob to cope with James, but if the message which they had received tallied with mine I did not blame them for taking this mode of action.

The front door of the house leading to James's flat was open. His flat was situated on the first floor and the entrance door leading to his flat could normally be seen. Not on this occasion however! A dark figure, holding an axe in its right hand, blocked the view! Standing at the front door of the house I would not be honest if I did not admit I would have wished to be anywhere else except here. I was terrified! I would have given anything to be able to swop my position with the police officers and sit in their mini. In my haste to leave the surgery I had forgotten to bring James's medical records with me, and a frightened quick look up the almost-dark stairs had served to blank out my memory. I had only been able to have a cursory look at the figure at the top of the stairs. I could not for the life of me recall ever having previously seen him.

Miss Dooley, now came to join me at the entrance of the house and explained the whole situation. She knew James very well, but he had threatened her when she had made an attempt to go up the stairs and this is why she had sent both for the police and for me. At the time, I do not believe that I was paying much attention to what she was saying: my subconscious was working overtime at what lay in wait for me when I attempted to go up the stairs. I was also trying to connect James in some way with the practice. It was a futile exercise. I still could not place him.

It was no use: there was probably a full surgery of patients for me to see if I came out of this exercise alive with all my limbs intact. I could not afford to stand about any longer and waste time. In any event, someone had to do something. It was unfortunate for me that I had been the chosen one. I walked resolutely into the house through the front door into the downstairs hall. I looked up in the semidarkness to where this statue stood at the top of the stairs and could have shouted with joy. I breathed a sigh of relief. I knew him! I recognised him as the chap whom I had been treating for months for stomach trouble. He had attended regularly at monthly intervals for a check-up as I thought he might have a gastric ulcer and he had never given me any trouble! We had developed a *rapport*: to be truthful, I had become rather fond of the fellow. I cancelled my appointment with the undertaker. I also stopped sweating. I was *home and dry*! I have always had the gift of the gab, I knew I only had to put my bedside manner into overdrive to make headway with the axeman. I now pretended he had not kept his last appointment to see me. As I slowly climbed the dark stairs I shouted to him,

'a fine chap you are Jimmy! You don't keep your last appointment and I have all the aggravation of coming to see you. I told you when I last saw you that you probably have a gastric ulcer. You must never run out of the tablets I gave you otherwise the ulcer will burst. By the way, have you got any left? Let me see!'

God is good! James looked at me as I slowly mounted the stairs, recognised me as a friend, put down the axe on the upstairs' landing; turned, and walked into his flat like a scalded cat. He kept mumbling as he walked into the flat but I did not hear one word. I was not listening. He had put the axe down. I was safe! I was overjoyed at the turn of events and proceeded to walk up the stairs in my normal bouncing fashion as if it was the most natural thing in the world and entered his flat.

By the time I had reached the front door of his flat he had already passed through the entrance hall into his living room. I followed him into it. I had never had a visit to James before and what met my eyes startled me. The room was in complete disarray. It was a tip. All the walls had been crayoned on in an attempt to improve the decoration. It had been a disaster! There was no pattern. It looked as if someone had been playing noughts and crosses and never quite completed the game. Some art critic would most certainly have seen some design in this hideous mess: to me, who only likes paintings by Turner, Constable, Gainsborough and Canaletto, the scenes drawn on these walls were the product of a twisted mind.

The little furniture there was in the room was old and broken. There was not a decent chair to sit on. We held our conversation standing. He, propped up against the mantlepiece: I, against a rickety-old table which was threatening to deposit both me and it on the floor at any moment should I forget myself and put my whole weight on it. It was almost dark in the room, there was no light to be seen, but the streetlamp outside shone directly into this room and with no curtains we could see each other quite clearly. The streetlamp also demonstrated the fact that no windows in this flat had tasted water for many years.

All these observations flashed through my mind in seconds. My brain still remembered the axe and my tongue was searching for something to say to make him forget it. He had been looking at me hesitantly, then blurted out the reason why he had not been able to keep his last appointment.

'You see, I have been busy decorating the room and haven't had time to do anything else,' he said.

I looked around the room and pretended to be happy with his handiwork. I was naturally doing my best to humour the fellow. Besides, James was broad and muscular, a six-foot-tall chap and had he decided to change tactics and test me in a physical contest I would most certainly have come out on the losing side.

'My! My! you should have taken up painting as a profession,' I said; the conviction in my voice even frightened me because of its apparent sincerity.

'When did you last take the special tablets for your stomach?' I asked.

'I ran out of them yesterday,' was the answer.

It was just the answer I had hoped and prayed for. I took out some tablets from my medical bag –

largactil – a powerful sedative, and made him swallow some.

'It was a godsend I came today. We have stopped your ulcer from bursting,' I told him.

I spent the next ten minutes explaining what would happen to him if he did not take his tablets regularly and come to see me in the surgery for regular check-ups. The largactil had still not had the desired effect of making him drowsy and forgetful, so we spent the next five minutes discussing his painting and the state of his finances. The Almighty should forgive me! I even suggested to him that he might take up landscape painting and make a reasonable living at it! We then discussed the advantage of X-rays in a case such as his and I even got him to agree to come and see me and get a form for a barium meal examination in Dulwich Hospital.

At last, my medication began to work. He became more and more drowsy and stretched himself out in an old armchair which was in such a state of disrepair the seat touched the floor. It surprised me the chair had not fallen apart when he sat down, only threads of worn fabric appeared to be holding it together. He closed his eyes. As I continued to try to make conversation I noticed that he was progressively having difficulty in answering me. His speech became more and more slurred and he finally gave up the effort of trying to concentrate to continue the conversation. He turned on to his side and fell asleep.

I had solved the problem of the axe.

I went downstairs to Miss Dooley who had spent

her time shivering with cold in the downstairs hallway whilst I had been concentrating on James. She had purposely kept herself within earshot and knew that I was alright. Nevertheless, I could see her face shining with relief as she saw me come down the stairs. We went to the 'heavy mob' in the mini outside who had – whilst we had been in the house – had the foresight to call an ambulance. The two ambulance attendants with the four policemen then went into the house to carry James, anaesthetised, snoring heavily, into the waiting ambulance.

I went back to the surgery where the waiting room was full of patients waiting to see me. As I walked through the waiting room I must have looked somewhat tired and dishevelled: one wag remarked loudly,

'these doctors go for their afternoon nap and forget to get up on time!'

*   *   *

The year 1970 I shall always remember, all my *loony* patients decided to come out of hibernation to pester me and increase my work load.

A twenty-eight-year-old white lad, called Dennis, who lived in Danby Street – a stone's throw away from the surgery and who had never previously shown any signs of mental disturbance, suddenly decided in February 1970 this situation had to change. He became depressed and refused to go to work. His work was that of a cashier in a bank and he had, according to his parents, always liked his work. He now however refused to leave home, sat in a chair all day long, complained of constant headaches, rumblings in his head and generally feeling unwell. He complained that his legs were so weak he was only able to negotiate the stairs with difficulty. As the toilet was downstairs, outside the back door, he had now taken up residence in the living room on the ground floor. The house, except for the kitchen, had only one room downstairs; his parents had been forced into the position of being under each other's feet.

Dennis would not stay in bed. He claimed he was not ill enough to remain there besides, in his opinion, he would be more trouble to his parents if he did so. In any event, he insisted that he only had a bad cold even if his parents thought he had influenza. His parents spent two days nursing him before they decided that both their diagnoses were almost certainly incorrect and that it was time I was called in to see him.

It was a dull, rainy, miserably-cold day, and in my stupidity I did not make the effort of taking an umbrella. I remember getting soaking-wet while walking to do this visit. His parents, who were quite old, were full of apologies for having to trouble me, but in the circumstances explained they had not known what to do for the best. Dennis had refused to leave his chair to visit the surgery and had become violent when they had pressed him to do so. His father told me that he had never previously had any trouble from the lad, he had been a very good son. Dennis had, since the family had moved into Danby Street, always paid the rent for the house and indeed had treated his parents with the greatest of respect. They loved him. They believed he had always loved them. Dad could only surmise that Dennis had had a quarrel with his girl friend to have brought him to this state. His girlfriend had been in touch, but they had prevented her from visiting him as they had believed he was suffering from influenza and could be infectious. They were now not quite so sure they had done the right thing.

Dennis was sitting in the lounge when I arrived and when he saw me looking like a drowned-rat he got up quickly and brought me a towel from the kitchen to dry myself. He must have forgotten momentarily that he had been complaining of weakness! I thanked him, we chatted and I deliberately spent some time drying myself to prolong the consultation. He appeared completely normal. He was lucid, friendly, talkative, not at all withdrawn and we had a quiet, intelligent conversation. We discussed politics, the football results, his favourite football team – he supported Manchester United although he had never seen them play – his girlfriend, and the health of his parents about which he expressed some concern. The strange thing was, unlike hypochondriacs, he did not even once mention any of his own symptoms. I really could not understand what the fuss was about.

I now began my serious questioning. He admitted to me he smoked too much, over twenty cigarettes a day. He also drank too much, about six-pints-of-beer a day. He suddenly burst out laughing.

'I have never been drunk in my life,' he said,

and he continued to smirk for some moments afterwards as if he had made a clever remark. This behaviour was certainly out of character! We all have our eccentricities, I thought the mention of drink could have brought out one of his.

I examined his chest and throat, then suggested to him he should lie down so that I could examine his abdomen: he raised no objection. Indeed, his behaviour was that of a model patient! He laid down on the sofa, pulled down his trousers, pulled up his shirt, and allowed me to examine him without any fuss. He even joked about his prominent navel – this was a small umbilical hernia – and he commented that a doctor at one time had told him to have an operation to remove it. The lump had been there for years, it had never given him any trouble, so why should he bother about it? We now spent the next few minutes discussing his hernia, what could go wrong in certain circumstances and I explained to him why his previous doctor had advised an operation. Whilst talking to him and palpating his abdomen I reduced the hernia with the greatest of ease. I knew that whatever this chap was suffering from his symptoms were not due to a strangulated umbilical hernia. After completing my physical examination I asked him to get up and return to a sitting position in his chair. He did exactly as he was told. I now tested his reflexes, they were all normal. I could find nothing physically wrong with the fellow.

Without warning, completely out of context, he blurted out he wanted to go on holiday to the Isle of Wight. I was taken completely by surprise. This statement had come out of the blue, neither of us had previously discussed holidays and certainly had made no mention of the Isle of Wight. One of my many failings is that I cannot take life seriously. We are on this planet for such a short time. I have always believed that we should try to enjoy every minute of it. I now came unstuck! In my nonsensical way I remarked,

'What do you want to go to the Isle of Wight for? It is probably bucketing down with rain there. I don't suppose for one minute the weather there is any better than it is here.'

My statement appeared to have an electrifying effect on him. He jumped out of his chair as if he had been shot. *He butted me in the head!* I staggered back. It was the first time in my life a patient had ever shown any belligerence towards me. I was more shocked than actually hurt. I wondered what was going to happen next. As suddenly as he had jumped up, he sat down again. With a vexed look on his face he said,

'I suppose, I shouldn't have done that!'

He appeared remorseful. I was extremely frightened. He had not only given me a headache but food for thought. I had never previously been in this situation – have never since – and must admit I honestly did not know how to cope with it. I did not now know when I next said anything I would provoke an even more violent reaction. I took the line of least resistance, the coward's way out. I gave his parents a prescription for largactil a very strong antipsychotic drug, and fled back to the surgery. After a strong cup of tea I telephoned the Maudsley

Hospital and asked for a psychiatric consultant to do an emergency domiciliary visit to Dennis's home. A psychiatrist telephoned me back to ask the reason for the urgency and after a chat agreed to see Dennis the same day, after his afternoon clinic.

He telephoned me after he had seen Dennis and said that he had found the whole situation bizarre. He had found Dennis to be completely normal. However, in view of my findings, and his unexplained behaviour towards me – someone he knew and trusted – he thought it dangerous to allow this man his liberty. The psychiatrist's actual words to me were,

'he knows you and head-butts you! Can you imagine what he will do to a stranger in the street who poses a similar stupid question! By the way, I mentioned the Isle of Wight to your patient and got no reaction. Perhaps it was the fact I forgot to mention it was raining there!'

Dennis was admitted into hospital under emergency mental section that same evening and was not released for three months. The diagnosis was, he was suffering from schizophrenia. I have seen him on hundreds of occasions since his release to renew his medication, but I am pleased to say he has given me no more psychiatric headaches.

Needless to say, whenever he has mentioned the need for extra-medication to tide him over a holiday I steer clear of mentioning the Isle of Wight! I also avoid making facetious remarks about the weather!

* * *

In 1970, Mr Patrick O'Reilly, aged forty-five years, one of my many Irish patients, found that he had so many problems life had become unbearable. To overcome his depression he had – until he made a decision to end it all – found his solace in the bottle. After a day's work on the building site he would drink himself stupid, come home rolling drunk, and expect his wife to clear up the mess he had created by his homecoming. She told me on more than one occasion that she would have preferred if he never came back home at all. When he sometimes arrived back in a worse condition than even she was prepared to tolerate she would throw him out to sober up in the garden.

She was a big woman, it did not take much effort on her part to pitch Patrick on to the lawn in the back garden, and she made no allowance for weather conditions. As she explained, he had obviously not given any thought before he came home as to whether he was sober or drunk, why therefore should she worry whether it was wet or dry outside. I often marvelled as to how Patrick managed not to succumb to attacks of pneumonia after being ejected on to a wet lawn in the winter. He would remain soaked to the skin for several hours, too drunk to get up, without even catching a cold. He just did not, or would not appreciate the problems he forced on his wife. His remark,

'a man must have a drink to get rid of the dryness in his throat after a day's work on the building site,' was a constant rejoinder to my reprimands.

What he purposely failed to remember was, his behaviour did not alter on Saturday or Sunday when he did not have to go to work. Dry throats, according to the teachings of Patrick, took several days of intensive treatment with alcohol to cure.

Patrick explained to me that Frances had been his childhood sweetheart before he had married her, she had therefore known his work and the problems associated with it. He had hoped she would understand his predicament. Unfortunately, she had not! It has to be inferred therefore that Patrick's marriage was not a happy one. In my opinion however, knowing the family as well as I did, his wife was certainly the innocent party. The couple had six young children, the eldest was only eight years old and Patrick just would not bring home enough money to feed and clothe them. It was not that he was not able to do so, he certainly earned enough, he was a skilled bricklayer, but drink costs money and when there was a conflict of interest between family and drink the family always came second.

I remember being on duty one Christmas Day, in the sixties, and going to visit a patient in Lyndhurst Square. As my car turned into Holly Grove from Bellenden Road – the one-way system did not exist in those days – I almost brought Mrs O'Reilly's day of deliverance from the man who plagued her life a step nearer. I nearly knocked Patrick down as he swayed from side to side along the edge of the deserted road. He kept staggering into the road from the pavement. Before the opportunity presented itself – if I had so wished – to deliver the *coup de grâce* on the road, he quickly staggered back on to the pavement. He must have read my mind! In my rear-view mirror I saw him sway back into the middle of the road after I had passed. This was at two o'clock in the afternoon, while his family was anxiously waiting for him to return so they could proceed with their Christmas dinner.

In 1970, he finally made up his mind his problem had become impossible to solve. Perhaps it was the devil drink which made up his mind for him! As neither the doctor nor priest were prepared to side with him in his conflict with his spouse there was only one solution – end it all! If eternal damnation was to be his lot – so be it. He could not, and would not, give up the bottle. Even a *thicko* like Patrick had now worked out that he was faced with a financial dilemma. Something would have to be sacrificed. The money left over from his drinking bouts was now not enough to cater for his family's basic needs. When he came home from work he now found there was a shortage of food in the house. Only one solution remained!

Six weeks after he had made his decision to end his life which would have released his wife from a life of humiliation, degradation and poverty, one of my partners was astonished to receive a letter from Patrick, marked private and confidential. Patrick had purposely not written to me. I knew of his impossible behaviour towards his wife and what was more important, he knew that I knew. He was hoping my partner who did not know him would have more compassion, besides, hc was banking on the fact my partner was of the same faith. He knew that if he had written to me in the vein which he had written to my partner he would have received a hurtful reply. He wanted money, not insults!

The letter explained Patrick's predicament in detail. My partner showed it to me. I read it with admiration at the gall of the man! He began with apologies for attempting to commit a sin and he hoped that my partner – whom he knew to be a God-fearing man – would have it in his power to forgive him. He knew that he had been a sinner in attempting to take his own life. There must be some goodness in him, my partner must have realised this, the Blessed Virgin had saved him! Without wishing to cause offence to my many catholic friends and blaspheme, if he believed this, it would mean the Blessed Virgin did not know him as well as I did. He was writing from a bed in Southend General Hospital, where he was being subjected to a period of abstinence. It was killing him! My partner, he continued, would understand this! My partner – who was looking over my shoulder – saw the astonished look on my face as I read aloud this piece and remarked, '*bloody cheek!*'

Patrick explained that he had gone to Southend so that his wife and family could have a new start in life without being pestered by a sinner like himself. The insurance policy on his life would, he believed, have been enough to allow his family this new start. He knew he was committing a cardinal sin by taking his own life, but this could not be as bad as people would make it out to be. By making this decision and taking this action he would be saving the lives of his wife and children! This logic I thought was erudite: knowing the fellow as I did, the enforced absence of alcohol was actually allowing his brain to work!

He had gone to Southend with the best of intentions, to get drunk and end his life. He had jumped off the pier and was sure everyone would have believed he had drowned accidentally. Instead of waking up dead, he had woken up in the Southend General Hospital, unable to move. He was in constant pain in his back, and legs, and was not allowed out of bed. He could not even get out of bed if he wanted to. His right leg was 'hung up' in the air over a pulley and although he tried to move he was unable to do so. It was like being in prison. My partner would understand! If I had not known what a gentleman my partner was I would have become paranoid at what kind of a man I had chosen to work with from the contents of this letter.

Patrick continued, the nurses in the hospital were not even prepared to provide him with a bottle of beer. He had spoken to the doctors and they had ignored his request. They had laughed at him when he said that life without a pint was not worth living. My partner, whom he had always regarded as a friend, a pious man, a compassionate man, a saint, surely would not refuse a fellow the price of a couple of pints. The cheek of the man! He had been a patient of mine for years, my partner had never ever met the fellow; he only knew him by reputation.

The hospital reports, which followed a week after Patrick's letter, confirmed the story of his fall and elaborated on the details. Patrick had jumped off the pier as his letter stated and he had indeed fooled the authorities: the hospital report claimed he had fallen off the pier accidentally. Patrick had

130

obviously forgotten to confirm the times of the tides. Instead of falling into the sea as was his intention and drowning himself he had fallen on to a patch of hard sand under the pier and fractured his pelvis and femur. He had been found at eleven o'clock at night, moaning and groaning, by a couple exercising their dog. It was the dog who had actually found him. It had been pitch-dark at the spot, the couple had passed without spotting him or noticing anything unusual. Their dog however must have liked the alcohol fumes being exhaled from Patrick's gaping mouth. In its excitement, it had chased around him sniffing vigorously, barking like mad. They had gone back to fetch the dog and had then found the cause of the dog's attention. Patrick had been saved by a dog! The couple had realised immediately from the way that he was lying there were some bones broken and had called an ambulance. They believed, as anyone in their right mind would have done, Patrick had fallen off the pier accidentally.

In the final part of his letter Patrick wrote cursing his bad luck. Never in his whole life had he been able to do anything right! Once again came the phrase, my partner would know exactly how he felt! All he now wanted was a few pounds to tide him over a critical period of his life so that he could make a fresh start.

My partner has never told me whether he answered this letter, but of one thing I am certain – he did! It was obviously couched in terms not to Patrick's liking! Six weeks after Patrick's letter to my partner was received, Mr Patrick O'Reilly left my medical list and transferred his *fumes* to another doctor.

*   *   *

My knowledge of psychiatric problems in 1953 had been three lectures in medical school – I skipped the others as the examination paper in the finals only had one question on the subject and this could be substituted – and the occasional patient who came in complaining of symptoms which defied my understanding of anatomy. My only experience of psychiatry was the army consultant who used to pay regular visits to the casualty reception station in Neumünster when I was doing my army service there. This fellow used to come to my home for lunch and he had the habit of standing up during the meal and wandering aimlessly round the room. My wife Louise often questioned his sanity and I was therefore thrown into general practice believing that there was not such a wide gulf between being a psychiatrist and somewhat mentally abnormal.

The patient who complained of pain in his left ear which travelled down his spine to his belly, caused him to pass wind all the time, gave him an excruciating cramp in his left heel may indeed have been physically ill, but was also in my opinion a *nutcase,* a psychiatric problem. Schizophrenia, as a disease, was to me a text book definition for a person with a split personality, a Jekyll and Hyde character, but as I had never met a case in general practice I was quite unable to diagnose it.

I was therefore quite unprepared to deal with Stanley Harvey, aged twenty-one, who lived in Choumert Road in 1953, and who called into my surgery every few days to see me in case I wanted for anything. He would call at the evening surgery on his way home from work, discuss the weather, and offer to provide help in any way he could to the young chap who had become his doctor, who had just started in practice in Peckham.

I used to enjoy his company for our discussions would not be about medicine but about cars. He was a car mechanic and as he had only recently completed his apprenticeship he was naturally enthusiastic about them. Money however had been tight and he had not as yet been able to afford one of his own. I had recently bought a second-hand Ford myself, this was the best I could afford at the time and he used to give me useful advice on its maintenance. In those days I was not averse to climbing under a car to do my own repairs.

He told me during one of our conversations that he knew of certain people who were prepared to injure me and ruin my practice. As I knew as fact one of the local general practitioners did not welcome my settling in Peckham, I did not know whether to believe him or not. Attempting to drive me away from the area I could have believed, the injury part however somehow did not ring true. I would never have believed that a colleague would have gone to such lengths as to hurt a fellow for a few hundred patients. He would have had to be certifiable!

'Not to worry!' Stanley said, after he had warned

me of the danger; he would protect me from all my enemies.

After this conversation, I used to see him standing in all weathers, at odd times, on the corner, at the other side of the road outside the Post Office, watching our house. I must be honest, I did not pay as much attention as I should have done. He had a regular job, he was a good-looking young chap and I thought he was waiting for a girlfriend. When he had told me people were prepared to injure me, I thought he meant financially. By no stretch of the imagination did I ever conceive that he meant physically. I was wrong in my diagnosis.

At 1.30, in the afternoon of Christmas Day, 1954, there was urgent knocking on the surgery front door. We lived on the premises at the time and I answered the door myself. It was Stanley's sister, Doris. She was breathless, incoherent, she almost fell into the passageway when I opened the door. I had only been in the practice for a short time and I did not know this young lady; her breath too made me hesitate for it smelt as though she had spent the whole morning gargling with alcohol. I did not know what to believe! As the only information I could get out of her as she forcibly pulled at my jacket was that her mother was seriously ill I had no option but grab my medical bag and run back with her to her house.

Her mother was indeed seriously ill! She had been stabbed in the stomach by Stanley who was wandering aimlessly about the house. Luckily, the wound had not penetrated any vital organs. The attack had caused the mother to faint and Stanley pass into a *catatonic* state.

I arranged for Mrs Harvey to be admitted to St Giles Hospital as an emergency, and from Stanley's abnormal mental behaviour, rather than treat the matter as a purely criminal affair, after notifying the police, had him admitted to a mental hospital.

What had triggered off the attack Stanley's sister later told me, was an argument which he had had with his mother over his Christmas dinner. She did not like stuffing, never had, but had always stuffed the turkey to please the family. The family was a poor one. In preparation for the Christmas dinner of that year, counting pennies, Mom had simply forgotten to buy ingredients for stuffing the bird. Rather than deny the family a turkey she had served it up *unstuffed*. When Stanley's portion had been served to him he had gone berserk!

It was then that I found out why Stanley's father – although registered with me as one my patients – had never been to see me. He had been for years a patient in the same mental home to which I had just sent Stanley!

* * *

A general practitioner is often fooled over his diagnosis until he actually gets to know his family. I had an experience in 1957 which taught me that life is never as it appears in the first instance.

Mr Heason (Bob), was an income tax inspector, married to a German girl, whom he had met while serving in the Forces in Germany. He had known nothing of her background: her parents had been killed in a British air raid on Hamburg in 1944, and no other members of her family had survived the 1939-1945 war. There was not much to be said about the match, she was an extremely-pretty girl and he had fallen in love. Bob Heason had been a corporal in the Royal Army Service Corps and his officers had used every device to try to stop him marrying this girl – all to no avail. He married her in 1950: I was left with the problems of sorting things out when Bob was demobilised and the couple settled in Talfourd Road, Peckham, and became patients of mine in 1954.

Mr Heason had served in Berlin. I have never been to Berlin. I have never been fortunate enough, even though I spent the whole period of my duty whilst serving in the Forces, in Germany. Berlin was a difficult place to get to when I served in Germany, it was surrounded by East Germany and East Berlin was controlled by the Russians. In 1949, the only way of getting to Berlin overland from the West was in convoy and as even convoys had problems, Berlin had been supplied by air. I was the lucky fellow who only had one posting during my whole army service. This was to Neumünster in Schleswig-Holstein on the 100 up, the cobbled, barrel-shaped road which linked Germany to Denmark and only a few miles from the Danish border. I spent my leave in Copenhagen, near the Rialto, in the Mission Hotellet, next door to a brothel – a much more exciting experience than in West Berlin. Breakfast time in this hotel was amusing, my wife and I used to gape as we watched the wondrous sight. The hotel, as it can be gathered from its name, was a religious hotel mainly occupied by commercial travellers and the men would be on their knees praying, before partaking of their morning repast. This, after having spent the night next door!

Mrs Heason had been born in Hamburg, had spent her childhood there and as Hamburg is near Neumünster and I knew the place well we quickly developed a rapport. To be perfectly honest she was good to look at, and as her English was poor she preferred to speak in her native tongue; it was a useful way of practising my German.

Bob always came to my surgery accompanied by his wife and as he suffered from nerves he was a frequent visitor to my premises. His main problem was; his family had never become reconciled to the fact that he had married a German girl – the enemy. His father and mother had simply refused to accept the marriage and had broken off the relationship which they had previously enjoyed with him. He was one of six children, three brothers and two sisters. And although they tolerated his presence in their homes they absolutely forbade entrance to his wife – the *German bint*. I suppose a good deal of resentment could be traced to the fact that one of the brothers had been lost fighting the Germans in Crete. They simply could not understand how one of the family could possibly have formed a liaison with a German. Bob was a friendly chap, with a friendly outgoing personality, and he suffered greatly from the family hostility. It came therefore as no surprise to me that Bob had 'nerve problems'.

The only recreation Bob had, apart from his wife, was his visit to the local pub every evening on his way home from work. The trouble was even here he could not relax. He could never enter into discussion about his work. On the one occasion he had been foolish enough to drink too much and mention what he did for a living he had staggered home with two broken ribs and a bloody nose – a present from the other drinkers in the establishment. People just do not like tax inspectors, especially when the inspectors have the audacity to fraternise. They could be spies!

I have already stated Bob's wife was a pretty young woman: she was not just pretty, she was gorgeous. With lily-white skin, blonde hair flowing down her shoulders almost to her waist, the bluest eyes imaginable, she was the *epitome* of one's description of the perfect *Aryan*. Added to her attraction, she was always immaculately dressed. She came to see me regularly for gynaecological problems. Perhaps more often than necessary. Probably just to chat about the evil family she had married into. She was only twenty years old in 1957 and as she had spent the war as a child in air-raid shelters, as many of us had done in this country, she was just too young to understand her husband's family hatred and hostility. I spent a good deal of my time at every consultation in advising her to be patient. I told her that as I was Jewish I had no cause to love her nation, but as she was a nice person she had to adjust to the fact it would take many years before her new family would accept her.

One day, she turned up in my surgery in a wild and dishevelled state. Her husband, she announced, was spying on her. He suspected her of taking men into the house when he was at work, and it had now reached the stage when he had posted a man at the corner of the road watching the house. When she looked out of her bedroom window she could see the chap quite distinctly. Always the same chap, but what could she do when she was innocent. She had never entertained men in her house and everyone knew it. In any event, her English was too poor to have a decent conversation with anyone. The only men she knew were her husband's friends and they only came with him. She was now in fear of her life! Her husband had gone insane! She would like me to get him *put away* for her safety.

I humoured her, told her that I would do what I could to get her husband *'locked up'* and when her husband appeared at my surgery a few days afterwards, approached him in a round about way of his wife's allegations. To my amazement, he showed no surprise.

'I would give anything to be locked up away from her,' he said. This was even before I had yet mentioned the locking up to him!

'She is impossible to live with. She is paranoid. She often goes out into the street and stops people to tell them to save her from me as I am poisoning her. She is a terribly lonely girl. Her English is poor and she is not strong enough to brave-it-out when being laughed at when shopping. Not having any of her own family alive, now shunned by mine, she has become a 'nutcase'. She honestly believes I have men posted at the corner watching her. She has actually gone over to men at times accusing them of working for me. What would you think doc if a pretty girl

139

whom you have never previously seen in your life came over to you at the corner of a street to speak to you in broken English? She has obviously got to be a prostitute touting for custom, or a nutcase. It does not take a bloke long to decide in what category my wife falls.'

I now did not know whom to believe. Bob had always been a 'bag of nerves' and his wife had always appeared to me to be the more stable of the two. The only immediate thought which sprung to my mind was, we could now have them both *locked away*! Two days after his appearance at my surgery, the problem as to who was the real *nutcase* was solved for me by the police. They sent for me urgently, to attend Bob who had injuries on his shoulder awarded to him by his wife, with the help of an axe.

Bob had been sitting with one of his friends at the table in the dining room doing his pools when the incident had occurred. Now Bob had a witness as to who was the *barmy* one. His wife had come into the room naked! While they had been looking in amazement at this strange mode of dress they had forgotten to notice what she was wielding in her right hand. At the shock of seeing this apparition, Bob and his pal had stood up. Bob alone had then been singled out for attack. The lady had been in a mad frenzy, had aimed a blow from a chopper to Bob's head, but Bob had ducked. The chopper had thankfully shaved past his head, not struck it. She had missed his head! She had failed to score a bulls eye! She had however scored some points, she had caught him on the shoulder. Luckily for Bob his friend had been present, it had taken the strength of both of them to disarm and overpower her. They had been forced to tie her arms behind her back with a scarf before they had found it safe to call the police. Bob, when he related the story, told me that he and his friend had had such a struggle to overpower his wife, at the time, they wondered whether they would be able to do so. Although she was a slightly-built girl, in her madness, she had found unbelievable strength. The police had taken her away kicking and screaming, accused by her of being in league with her mad husband.

When she reappeared at my surgery several months later, she was calm and relaxed. The medication which she was receiving from the mental hospital was keeping her balanced and under control. She gave me no further problems.

Mr Heason was transferred by the Inland Revenue to a place in Yorkshire in the sixties and the couple therefore had been obliged to find themselves a new doctor. I heard from one of their acquaintances some time later that Mrs Heason had gone missing on the moors and after a search had been found dead. She had evidently taken her own life by taking an overdose of barbiturates! The only things in her possession at the time were some tablets, a map of Germany, and a German-English dictionary.

5

Coffins

Most of my West Indian patients who came into this country in the fifties were able to become assimilated into the area. A few however became so disillusioned, no amount of persuasion on my part would alter their beliefs that we were a racialist society. Whatever their feelings towards the rest of society they rapidly became friends of mine: I liked their sense of humour and outgoing personalities. They were a tremendous amount of fun even though at times I was the object of their merriment. Some however carried their conviction we were racialists to the extreme and believed it persisted even after death.

I had just completed an exhausting evening surgery in 1981 and at eight o'clock at night I got into my car in the forecourt to drive home. I was feeling extremely tired, but was shaken out of my lethargy when I started the car – it jumped about like a *bucking bronco*. I quickly turned off the engine fearing an explosion. Very gingerly I started the car again. Although the engine sprung into life immediately and appeared to be working normally I was almost thrown out of the driving seat by the convulsions the car was making. It was being jerked up-and-down as if on a trampoline and was being shaken side-to-side as if travelling over a rocky road. The car was a Ford Fiesta, it had never previously given a halfpennyworth of trouble and I had done my house calls in it that same afternoon without any hint of a problem. At the end of an exhausting day, to give me aggravation, it was now being *bloody-minded*! In my tired state, I just could not even begin to think what the fault could be. I switched off the engine and got out to check under the bonnet. It was then that I heard squeals of laughter from under the car. It was my old pal Hubert West, a tall, extremely-fit, muscular West Indian, playing games with his doctor. He was lying face upwards under the back of the car and had shaken it up-and-down whenever I had attempted to start it.

Miss Adlyn Crowe, a young-looking, fifty-five-year-old Trinidadian, was looking very pleased with herself after a trip to Trinidad in 1979. When I asked her why, she told me she had gone over to buy a funeral plot for herself. Now I knew this lady was a bundle of fun and could be teased without taking offence so I remonstrated with her. I told her she could have saved herself a good deal of money if she had been prepared to allow herself to be buried in this country. After all, I said, if she expected me to pay her the respect of accompanying her on her last journey, there was no way I was going all the way to Trinidad to do so. She was also going to put me to a lot of trouble in getting her body shipped out. In the first place, an ordinary death certificate would not be sufficient, I would have to get an export licence – incidentally this is the truth. Then there was the question of the coffin. An ordinary wooden coffin would not stand the journey, she would require a lead one. If she was going by air, had she given any thought of how much a metal coffin would weigh and what the cost of the transport would be. I looked at her.

'You're fat, you will require a coffin which weighs a ton!', I said.

She just looked at me and gave a sardonic smile.

'I'm afraid you don't understand doc! Do you know what happened to my friend?' she said.

'She died in St Thomas' Hospital about 4 months ago, and her husband had her buried here. I can't blame him for doing so as my friend had cancer and hasn't been able to work for years. They were only living in a council flat and there was no way he could have afforded to have his wife taken home for burial. I went to the funeral and do you know what they did? They opened up a grave with coffins already in it! There must have been about a dozen coffins already in that grave and I wouldn't be surprised if they are not going to put more in. Her coffin is going to be mixed-up with all the other coffins. How do you know the people in the other coffins like black people?'

She had won the argument. I had no answer.

In the winter of 1985 there was a strike of gravediggers, the weather was so bad there was a backlog for burials and a queue developed. Adlyn, like many of my West Indian patients, had high blood pressure, and I monitored her regularly for this. When she came to see me on one of her

144

regular appointments she complained bitterly about the gravedigger strike and what she thought of people in this country who could behave in this fashion.

She explained that a few weeks earlier another of her friends had died and had still not been buried. When I had previously spoken to her about the purchase of a plot for herself in Trinidad I had laughed at her. Now what had I to say for myself! She had been right in buying her plot and making funeral arrangements to be buried in Trinidad. When I now heard of the expense of being buried in this country I would apologise to her for even doubting her. This friend of hers awaiting burial in this country had already cost the family over eight-hundred pounds. This was not the end of the story, the undertaker was continuing to charge the family for storage. The body was in the undertaker's mortuary and had already been there for three weeks.

'God only knows when she will be buried,' she continued.

The undertaker had already billed the family for storage and would not release the body until the eight-hundred pounds had been paid. They had been forced to pay the money and had left the body with the same undertaker for no one else was prepared to bury her. They still didn't know when she would be buried or even what the final cost was going to be. If her friend had listened to Adlyn and arranged to be buried in the West Indies nothing like this would have happened.

Adlyn had already scored one victory over me when she had first booked her homeward passage in the

145

'box' and I had no intention of letting her score again without putting up a desperate fight. I now had to think very quickly.

'When your friends booked your friend's funeral what did they say to the undertaker?' I quipped.

She looked at me perplexed.

'Well,' I continued; 'the family may have booked in incorrectly. When they booked the funeral they should have stipulated that in the event of a dispute and storage required the body did not require bed and breakfast – room only'!

*   *   *

Visits in my early years in practice were always numerous and trying to build up a medical list made it imperative that I always did them as soon as humanly possible. I also did far more repeat visits than a doctor would normally do in order to get my face and reputation well known in the area. This practise of mine inevitably ended up by my making a rod for my own back when I had a large enough list of patients and no longer needed to build up the practice. As I did not regard Sunday as a rest day I always made a point of doing repeat visits on this day and I had a very uncanny experience on one of these days on a visit to a patient in Lyndhurst Grove. Many of the houses have three floors: it had to be my luck my patient occupied a bedsitter on the third floor!

The year was 1966, and the young lady whom I was visiting was recovering from a severe attack of glandular fever. I had already visited her a couple of times, but she was the only person in that house at the time who was my patient: the occupants of the other rooms did not join my list until a much later date. I had been let into the house by a fellow on the ground floor whom I did not know and although the stairs were steep I skipped up them without any distress. After all, the young lady whom I was going to see was worth running to! Although she was still in bed, she had recovered enough to have a discussion with me about her future as she had no family in London. She wanted to know how much longer she would have to remain in bed, how long her illness would last, and how long she would have to be away from work.

The only matters we did not discuss were the occupation and habits of the remainder of the house in which she lived, and whether they were alive or dead. She did not tell me that a member of the household who lived on a lower floor had departed his or her life and was waiting to be collected by the undertakers. She also forgot to tell me that the carpet on the stairs leading to her room had worked loose. Perhaps she thought she did not have to. I would quickly learn about the carpet myself as I stepped out of her room to descend the stairs.

On the second stair down, I could be mistaken, it may have been the third, the carpet under my feet slipped. I lost my footing. I felt such a fool as I hurtled down the stairs. But what is strange I still had enough presence of mind to consider what part of my anatomy I should sacrifice to save my life.

There was no doubt at all that I was going to fracture something, but the extent, and the parts, were the main occupation of my mind as I charged down the steep stairs.

I had not released my hold of my medical case, but it was torn from my grasp on the landing between the second and first floors when the handle of the case became entangled with a door handle leading to one of the rooms. I was forced to let go. I had no wish to hang on and lose an arm! This collision with the handle swung me around, increased my momentum, and caused me to lose complete control. I fell down the last remaining steps from the first to the ground floors no longer caring what the future held for my body. At that precise moment in time, a coffin was being manouvered through the front door into the downstairs' passage by Mays, the undertakers in Rye Lane. They had come to collect a body on the first floor.

I had a lucky fall. I fell on to the top of the empty coffin! Both the coffin and MY BODY went crashing to the ground. The bearers, who had been forced to let go by my weight and the force of my descent looked down at me in astonishment as I lay stretched out on the top of the conveyance. One of the chaps recognised me.

'Well doc, I have now seen everything,' he said.

'I have seen plenty of people stretched out in one of these coffins, never, ever, one on top. Until today, I have also never seen anyone who wanted to jump into one of these things. Still, there is always the first time!'

That coffin had certainly saved me from breaking my neck. I had fallen down sixteen steps and they were steep ones too. Who would ever have credited the fact that a coffin could be a life saver!

*　*　*

The Molineuxs were a family who intrigued me for their name did not appear to betoken their Scottish ancestry. There was no doubt however when one met Robbie Molineux and he opened his mouth where he was born. His Glasgow accent shone like a beacon. He was a five-foot nothing chap, who always had trouble with the police; they with him. To be honest, the police liked him. He was the old-fashioned burglar who pitted his wits against theirs and he was quite prepared to say, *'it's a fair cop,'* when he ended up a failure. He spent a lot of his time behind bars, he was however only a small-time crook so the periods of being shut away were consequently short ones.

In 1957, after having spent six months *inside,* he came to explain to me about his stomach ulcer for which I had treated him before he had been incarcerated. I had, in his opinion, been an angel in my treatment of his condition,

'you should see how they treat you inside!' were his actual words.

Needless to say, I did not volunteer to accompany him on one of his missions so that I could take up his offer and put his statement to the test. I had always stressed to him the necessity of taking regular meals for his ulcer and at that time the taking of a meal every two hours was considered essential for the healing process. Unfortunately, he complained he had been unable to eat the prison food.

'It is diabolical, not even fit to be fed to rats. You should try it yourself.' he said. Once again he was inviting me to accompany him on one of his fruitless missions. I made no comment.

After a general chat about life in prison, I repeated the treatment which had preceded his internment as a guest of Her Majesty. I insisted that he cut down on the number of cigarettes he smoked, not only should he take the tablets and medicine which I was prescribing – regularly, but food similar to the rat food which the prison doctor had prescribed. When I particularly mentioned rat food he did not blink, his mind was obviously elsewhere: it was presumably my insistence on regular intervals which appeared to be giving him the most anxiety.

He told me that as his daughter was getting married and he was having a hard time in balancing his budget he did not know whether he would be able to follow my instructions to the letter. I had not previously heard of his daughter's intended marriage and if one had seen his daughter Margaret one would have realised Robbie's concern. Only a blind man or a drunk could have coped with such an ugly face. And when I explained that getting drunk at the wedding would certainly not be beneficial to a healing ulcer you would have thought that I was a judge who had just sentenced him to death. In no way could Robbie, for all his grumbles, be said to be a depressive. He had pointed out to me when I had warned him of his problems with the police that one day he might get hurt,

'you should know better than anyone doc, you only die once!'

My statement over drink therefore only caused momentary depression – he was a happy soul. His ulcer was not due to his over-indulgence of alcohol or cigarettes, it was due to problems with his occupation. He regarded burglary as a profession and like all professions one is either good or bad at it: he obviously fell into the second category. He had never been violent. The modern-day crook who carries a gun and uses violent means of reaching his objective would have been anathema to him.

Robbie's daughter, Margaret, got married on Saturday afternoon, in Wisbech, in June 1957 – the bridegroom it must be pointed out was not a Scot – and I had the pleasure of treating Robbie's wife, Freda, in the surgery, on Monday morning after the wedding. Robbie brought her in early, as an emergency, so that I could put three stitches in the laceration on her nose and prescribe some treatment for her two black eyes. My first reaction on seeing the injuries – I thought she had been in a car accident – was to tell Robbie he should have taken his wife to hospital immediately after the collision. I was astounded to hear however that the collision had not been between two cars, but between Freda's two eyes and nose, and her new son-in-law's fists.

An altercation had taken place at the reception.

The son-in-law, obviously the worse for drink, had started an argument with Freda over the cost of the reception and who was paying for it. Freda and Robbie were paying for it: and in their opinion they thought he was pouring too much of their money down his gullet in liquid refreshment than was good for him. They told him so! Their son-in-law had not agreed. To give more force to his argument, he had used his right fist on Freda's face. At the time, when this story was being related to me, I thought it strange that Robbie was insistent it was his son-in-law's right fist which had done the damage. On reflection, it must have been to point out to me that his son-in-law was right-handed and was using his argument to the maximum effect. What damage would have been done to Freda's anatomy should the son-in-law have been ambidextrous, I shudder to think!

Luckily, some guests not related to the family and playing no part in the financial aspects of the feud came to the rescue. They pulled Freda away from the happy bridegroom. Should they not have done so, poor Freda would have borne the scars of the joyous occasion for the rest of her days. Perhaps I am wrong in this supposition: seeing Freda only a few weeks ago for attacks of cluster headaches she reminded me of the hurt which I had repaired all those years ago. The physical hurt I repaired at the time; the mental hurt however has remained: it has festered, although the incident took place nearly forty years ago.

Freda herself was an Aberdonian, proud of being a Scot, and when her father died thought it her duty to bring her mother down to London to live with her. She had two sisters who lived in Aberdeen, but they were married with growing families and their houses much too small to grant her seventy-three-year-old mother, who suffered from diabetes and hypertension, a room she could call her own. In any event, Freda had always been her favourite daughter; mom was rather fond of Robbie too. She also liked London, and as she told me to my embarrassment, she liked her new doctor down here – me! She had therefore decided to leave the land which she loved and come down to live with Freda and Robbie.

The wedding of her granddaughter and her daughter's smashed-up face had caused no little upset in the family, but she had not been surprised. She had always told her granddaughter not to mix the blood – her granddaughter should have married a Scotsman. The granddaughter's marriage, and her leaving the parental home, now meant there was ample space in Freda's house for grannie to move about. I believe this was really the deciding factor which had decided grannie to move to London. Unfortunately, grannie had been used to living in a closely-knit community, where everyone knows everybody else, where everybody's business is common knowledge; in London she felt completely isolated. The majority of people would have been overjoyed at the space and time available to her, these people however could never have lived in a small, closely-knit community. Both Freda and Robbie were away all day at work, she felt lonely and unwanted.

In 1963, she became homesick, and decided that as conditions in Aberdeen were still not suitable for her to take up permanent residence there, she would go back at frequent intervals to meet up with her old friends. She went up in the summer of 1963 to stay with one of her daughters and sent me back a picture postcard which read 'the weather is glorious: wish you were here'! I am conceited. Perhaps she was telling me something. Perhaps I could have saved her! She may have been a clairvoyant! When in Aberdeen for exactly four weeks, her diabetes went out of control, she went into a diabetic coma, and was dead in two days.

Problems now arose surrounding the death and I, not a member of the family, could only nibble at the periphery. For some reason, Freda's mother had expressed the wish not to be buried anywhere near her husband, not even in the same cemetery. To make sure the family would not be able to override her wishes she had actually taken the trouble of paying a deposit to the undertakers in Forest Hill Road, so that she could be buried in the cemetery close by. She had obviously not expected to die in Scotland. We now had a problem!

Although the hospital in which she died was prepared to give the family a death certificate it was not prepared to allow the body to be buried in its grounds, nor was it prepared to allow the body to remain in its mortuary to eternity. It was also not prepared to provide or pay for transport to take the body to London. *Impasse!*

Robbie got in touch with the undertakers in Forest Hill Road and they came up with the solution. They would send a hearse to Aberdeen and would bring back Freda's mom themselves. There was however one fly in the ointment – the cost. The price for doing so was going to be one hundred pounds. Now one hundred pounds in 1963 was a lot of money – a fortune. It has to be remembered however, there were no motorways at the time.

The firm of undertakers would have had to send two men up. It would have taken them more than a day to get up to Aberdeen, and the men would then have needed to stay in hotels overnight for at least two nights. The firm told Robbie that just driving up nonstop would take their drivers from 18 to 20 hours. They had quoted one hundred pounds as an estimate, there was no way they were prepared to accept the job for a price less than one hundred pounds. If the family themselves however could arrange for the body to be brought back to London, as a favour to the family, and as the funeral had been booked prior to death, they were prepared to send a hearse to collect the body from Robbie's house at any time, day or night, at no extra cost. As this compromise had been reached, and the family could not afford the expense of sending up a hearse to Aberdeen it was arranged that the family would bring Freda's mom back themselves.

Robbie's friend was a butcher, he had a van which he used for his work, and as he did not need the use of the vehicle at the weekend he agreed to loan it to Robbie to bring the body back. He also agreed to accompany Robbie to Aberdeen and act as a spare driver in 'taking the wheel' when Robbie felt that he needed a rest. They would go up on Friday night after it got dark, the roads would then be less congested and the journey less tiring. They hoped with a bit of luck to be in Aberdeen by Saturday lunchtime and after a few hours rest drive back to London on Saturday night. In this way, bringing back Freda's mom would not interfere with the friend's work schedule. He would have his van back to carry *real meat* on Monday.

Robbie and his pal drove up on Friday night as planned and had no problems, unless a puncture can be called a problem to two, young, fit and healthy men. This delay had been minimal: they arrived in Aberdeen on Saturday lunchtime as planned, tired, but happy at having made it with such little fuss. They had a meal, spent the afternoon sleeping in one of Freda's sisters' houses, and set out back to London on Saturday night – a little after midnight – with Freda's dead mom reverently wrapped in sheets in the back of the van.

After about five hours nonstop driving, they were still in Scotland, neither Robbie nor his friend could remember exactly where, they thought they saw a mirage, an all night cafe. Luckily for them it turned out not to be a mirage, it was a real cafe, and it was open. The opportunity was too good to be missed. They pulled up, got out, stretched themselves; then went in to buy a meal.

The cafe appeared to be full, most of the occupants were men, but what struck them as rather peculiar, there were a couple of skimpily-dressed young girls sitting and smoking at one of the tables. Some of the men at the tables were eating, some drinking, some smoking, some had their heads in their arms curled up on the tables taking the opportunity of having a quick *kip*. No one in the cafe, even though the girls were not bad lookers, appeared to be taking any notice of these girls. Robbie and his pal were starving, had a quick meal of sausage and chips and washed the meal down with several cups of tea: feeling rested they lit up cigarettes. This for some reason seemed to be some sort of a cue for the girls. One of them came over with a cigarette to ask for a light and having been given one decided that her friend should join her at their table. Robbie when he told me the story of the cafe laughed.

'You should have seen these girls at close quarters doc! When we first saw them when we came in we thought they looked a *bit of alright*. At our table, they had "tarts" written all over their faces!'

The girls having decided to join them was a reason for the two to make a hasty exit and with suitable apologies they went outside. They went to the lorry park. No van! They were certain they had parked it between two lorries. There would not have been enough space for another lorry to fill the space in which they had parked their van and that is why they had chosen it. The space had just been wide enough to accommodate their van. The van had fitted in like a glove. The two lorries were still there, but where their van and its occupant had been parked there was now just empty space.

'You don't think your mother-in-law has pinched my van!' was his pal's remark. Robbie did not smile. He was not amused. He was dumbstruck! Why in heaven's name would anyone want to steal a van with a dead body inside it? Besides, he was certain they had locked the van before leaving it. Panic now set in!

They ran back through the lorry park to the cafe but were really out of luck that night. They ran in a panic, not looking where they were going, Robbie's pal was nearly killed when a lorry which appeared to them to have suddenly materialised from outer space knocked him down. He was however only grazed, and the shock of this collision was perhaps a godsend. It momentarily cancelled out the extreme shock which they had suffered in losing Freda's mom. It brought them to their senses!

On arrival at the cafe and explaining their predicament to the waitress, even before they had finished their story they noticed her attitude was hostile.

'I am fed up with you van drivers getting your vehicles "pinched",' she said.

'You're like a lot of babies who need their bottoms wiped. Why the hell don't you take out your rotor arms like the lorry drivers do?'

Robbie was in no mood for bandying words. After he had explained he was not so concerned about the van but about its contents and what the contents actually were, the girl changed her attitude. She became quite agitated.

'I don't want to work any longer than I have to and get held up by being involved in a murder mystery' she said, as she held the phone in her hand dialling for the police.

Within five minutes there was a police car at the

cafe. It only took another five minutes before they were told where their van was parked. The unusual sight of a van with its headlights full on, all its doors wide open, its engine running and parked at the side of a main road with no occupants had attracted the attention of drivers who passed it. Usually, when there was an incident and the driver was in trouble, he stood at the side of the road and waved for help. One driver stopped his vehicle to give help and finding no one near the van switched off the engine. He thought this would attract the driver back. No one came.

He went to inspect the contents. Horror of horrors! When he looked at what lay wrapped in a sheet in the van he nearly fainted. He ran back to his lorry and telephoned the police from the nearest phone box. The police went immediately to investigate and finding an unwanted corpse they suspected foul play. The neighbouring police forces were informed of the finding and all police forces were instructed to find the owner of the van as a matter of urgency to see whether he could throw some light on the affair. The phone call from the cafe had therefore delighted the police, they could now call off their manhunt and settle down to deal with the more mundane matters of solving real crime.

The van, when Robbie and his pal were taken to it by a police car from the cafe, was a sight. It had never had such attention in its whole life! There were four police cars, an ambulance, and a fire rescue vehicle surrounding it. A photographer was there taking photographs of the van and Freda's mom in all her nakedness. She had never had so many photographs taken of her and from so many positions when she was alive, certainly not when unclothed! The police regarded the abandonment of the van as obvious. The thieves, having stolen the van with its valuable contents wrapped up in a sheet had parked at the side of the road at a safe distance from the cafe to examine the loot. They had panicked when they had found out what lay beneath the carefully-wrapped sheets. The last thing they had in mind was to get involved in a murder. They had fled. They had not even bothered to turn off the engine.

Freda's mom was driven home without further incident. I saw Robbie a few days after he returned home as I was called out to see him as an emergency. He was running a high temperature and had taken to his bed. He was only suffering from an attack of tonsillitis, but the visit was lucky for me, otherwise this story would never have seen the light of day.

Robbie, in the few previous occasions I had seen him, had always regarded illness as a nuisance. Now, he appeared sullen and morose.

'You just can't understand women,' he said; when I asked what bothered him.

'I told Freda what happened at the cafe: why we were so late in getting back. You would have expected some thanks for bringing her mom back safely even if the old lady was dead. Freda wasn't at all grateful, she went f...... mad!'

'How could you possibly think of leaving mom all alone in the middle of the night, in a van, in a car park?' she screamed.

'You know mom hated to be left alone! That's the trouble with you Rob, you've got no respect!'

I gave Rob an injection of penicillin for his tonsillitis and a prescription. I made no comment. I thought it wise to keep out of the argument. I am a coward. Freda could hear every word from the next room.

The couple left my medical list in 1963 as they emigrated to Tasmania. I did not hear from them for seven years until, one morning, while doing a consulting surgery, in 1970, I was astonished to get a message from my receptionist; there was a phone call for me from Tasmania.

It was Robbie! He was, from his voice, very much the worse for drink. In a drunken Scot's drawl he told me he had just phoned to wish me a *happy new year*. I did not know how to reply. I was lost for words. It was *May*!

I have not heard from him since.

*   *   *

Young men are fond of cars, all kinds of cars find their enthusiasts, but I have never met an enthusiast like John Hampton. With a name like John Hampton he had to be English, nothing however was further from the truth. He was a Greek Cypriot, married to a Greek-Cypriot girl called Lisa, his father had been in the British army stationed in Cyprus and had married a Greek girl. When his father had been demobilised he had settled down in Cyprus to be near his wife's family and John had been brought up as a Greek. I learned a good deal of the culture of the Middle East from my frequent meetings with this young man, his wife Lisa, and her large family, who were all my patients.

I knew this couple before they were married: she was a young lady of nineteen who had a spotty face and drove me mad with her frequent visits to the surgery in attempting to find a cure, when I had none. I would never have dared to suggest the contraceptive pill might have helped. She was such a forthright character, her culture was such that she would have taken offence at the mention of the word contraceptive. She lived with her parents in the immediate area of the surgery. I cannot mention the exact location for fear of identification, but I can state that she was one of a family of five. She had three sisters, all younger than she was, and one brother, aged twenty-seven. This brother was the cause of concern to all the family for having been educated in this country he behaved like all his English contemporaries. He drank, smoked, went to dances with English girls and finally left to live with one.

John Hampton, the boy's brother-in-law, was a different kettle of fish: the loves of his life were not women, they were cars. All kinds, models, sizes and shapes; his desires had no limits. He loved car auctions and would often wander over the country looking for bargains. He was a barber by profession, a high-class hairdresser to be exact who, in spite of his love of cars, was not afraid of work. He took orders by telephone and would often go out in the evening to meet a particular customer's wishes at his home and stay working until late at night.

One night, he told his wife Lisa that he would not be returning home after seeing a customer. She should not worry. He was being driven down after work and seeing a potential buyer for one of his *bangers* to Exeter as a car auction was taking place there on the following day. He was taking a friend with him for company, another friend of theirs was driving down to Cornwall on business and would drop them off on the way. John knew Lisa would not be lonely for they lived with her parents and now she was doubly pleased; not only was John going to earn extra money, he was not even having to pay for the trip down. He told her that he would come back in the vehicle which he bought at the auction.

Lisa was not worried. In any event, she had an appointment with me that evening, her problem was not cars, it was her virginity. Every time she and John had attempted to make love, droopiness set in. She was still a virgin. They had been married for a year, but she had been too ashamed to report it to me earlier as they had both believed time would be the healer. They had tried all the remedies which were given to similar couples in answer to problems such as theirs in the agony columns of the press, without success. Her mother was disgusted that Lisa had now been married for a year and not presented her with a grandchild: this was the reason Lisa had plucked up courage to come and see me.

John went to Exeter as he had informed his wife and did exactly as he said he would do, he bought a vehicle and drove back to London in it. The family did not worry about John's whereabouts, they never did, he would often wander off to an auction in

Scotland and not return for a few days. The vehicles he brought back were not always in tiptop condition, some were *clapped-out bangers* and he lost money when he tried to sell them. Others however were a bargain and as John at the end of the year always ended up with a handsome profit no one really complained when he occasionally had a failure. There was one occasion when he had bought an old fire engine, everyone had laughed at him, he had however had the last laugh; it turned out to be a winner. He had converted the vehicle into a caravanette and made a lot of money.

John, besides being a hairdresser, ran a small used-car business, and having a charming personality and being a football fan made many friends. These friends were useful, they helped him to repair and renovate his old *jalopies*. It stretched one's imagination to classify these contraptions as motor vehicles, nevertheless, in the years since he had commenced his buy and repair business, only two vehicles had ended up as a dead loss in the junk yard.

One story related to me by John with a smile was when he had been a novice at the game and bought a Morris Minor with a revamped engine. He only had the car for two days, it was a dream, it went like a bomb. The previous owner had changed the engine from its usual one to a Ford V8 engine, and what fun he and his friends had in it the two days it was theirs. They drove to Brighton on the third day, the weather was glorious, and as they drove along they made a point of leaving the other cars standing! The cars which were being overtaken always thought from a distance that they were being approached by a racing car. These cars would tuck themselves into the near lane as far as safety would allow and the drivers would look astonished when they realised they were being pursued by a Morris Minor. To be truthful, the roar of John's engine sounded more like an aeroplane engine than a car and John admitted to me that he and his friends were themselves deafened by the noise of the engine.

They were roaring down Denmark Hill on the third day, having overtaken several cars on the way down to Camberwell Green when, to their horror, they noticed a set of traffic lights had been placed outside King's College Hospital, to enable pedestrians cross the road. This crossing had obviously been newly installed. John knew the road like the back of his hand, the crossing had definitely not been there when he had travelled this section in the previous week. Now, he had already passed Ruskin Park as he hurtled down the road before he had even noticed it! There was no way John was going to *beat* the lights. Even as he watched at the wheel of his car mesmerised, the lights changed from green to amber, then to red. Although he was still ten yards in front of the crossing, pedestrians on hearing an aeroplane engine bearing down on them suddenly hastened their steps to reach safety on the other side of the road. John slammed on the brakes.

The body of the car behaved impeccably. It stopped exactly on the white line which denotes the final parking spot for a car. The engine however did not have its own braking system: having been coaxed into believing that it was an aeroplane engine, it was now expected to behave as if it were a normal small car engine. It was having none of it! This was just too much to bear! No self-respecting V8 engine could be expected to tolerate a situation such as this. It decided to part company with the driver who expected it to behave in such a fashion. It left its mountings, hurtled through the radiator grill as if it were nonexistent, and deposited itself some fifteen to twenty feet in front of the car. Luckily, it had not hit anyone in its passage through the crossing. However, the din it made as it left the car and hurtled down the road gave it the satisfaction of revenging itself on its owner.

The nonappearance of John on the night after his attendance at the auction in Exeter was of no disappointment or concern to Lisa or her parents. They knew that he would return as soon as he could, any delay would not be due to wilfulness on his part. John's father-in-law always worked until 10.30 at night, he was self-employed, he owned a fish and chip shop in one of the roads which leads off Rye Lane. I remember the shop well, it did not smell of fish oil; it stank of it! I have to be fair to the chap, until his last illness I had rarely seen the fellow in the twenty-five years he was my patient. I had however always recognised his presence even before his appearance before me. He had been a nice chap, very respectful to his doctor. Whenever he had come to see me he had tried to mask the smell of fish and chips by soaking himself in *eau de cologne:* the bouquet of fried fish however had permeated through his clothes. He had not needed a visiting card. He had been a walking visiting card himself!

In the row of shops opposite the fish and chip shop was an undertakers and the odour of fish and chips is so pervasive many of the bodies who were interned in the chapel must have gone to their resting places in a patriotic spirit, with the smell of fish and chips in their coffins! I have been in this funeral parlour many times over the years, but to be honest I have never smelt fish and chips although I expected to do so. The heavy odour of incense could perhaps have concealed the smell. It could of course have been that the wind was blowing in the opposite direction! With the redevelopment of the area this funeral parlour has long since disappeared, so has the fish and chip shop, so have the owners of the shop who have become victims of the terminal illness called life!

One of the principal aggravations in John's father-in-law's life was this funeral parlour for it parked its hearse directly opposite his shop. He was a religious man, but for some inexplicable reason had a superstitious streak in him relating to death. He did not believe in the supernatural, death however worried him. Even the very mention of the word made him surreptitiously cross himself and he avoided looking across the road as much as he could. The parlour luckily was not immediately facing his shop: a dress shop was directly opposite with dressed mannequins in the window so he could fantasize his thoughts in this direction if he so desired. Some of the mannequins were armless, one was even legless, what fantasies he could have had with these I cannot imagine. What thoughts went through the minds of the bereaved as they passed this shop to arrange a funeral for their loved ones can only be surmised.

The dress shop however could not be blamed for having an undertakers next to it and it was after all a high-class one. It never smelt of fish and chips despite its proximity: it always smelt of roses. Gallons of perfume must have been needed daily to combat the smell of its 'rival'! I had been called on several occasions to visit this shop by the children of its owner although she was not my patient. She lived in Streatham and despite the fact she suffered from hypertension she would insist on coming in to work daily. She was in her seventies, her son and daughter who really ran the shop would have given anything to keep the old lady away from the place as she was such an embarrassment. She used to stand at the door of the shop waiting to pounce. As soon as she saw someone looking in the window she would be outside like a flash and almost drag the unwilling victim inside. Like a *praying mantis* who devours its mate, she used her forceful personality to such an extent that her children inside the shop would help the customer escape from her clutches rather than be a party to an unwanted sale.

The old lady was a friend of Mrs Nurse, who owned the flower shop in Peckham Rye, and who was a private patient of mine. Whenever the old lady at any time felt a little unwell I was asked to see her privately. It was not an easy task to perform: I did not relish having to see her although I knew I was going to be paid in cash. The only place available for examination was behind the counter and if a genuine customer came in I was in for a rough ride. The old lady honestly believed she was the only person capable of running the establishment. She would interrupt a sale even though I might be taking her blood pressure at the time! I often wonder what a person choosing a dress from the rack must have thought of the spectacle. There was this fellow with a stethoscope around his neck – a small, black, basket, clock-like thing on an old lady's elbow – holding a rubber ball in his right hand chasing the old lady who had a grey band bound tightly round the top of her arm. There was a definite connection between the band and the clock, there was rubber tubing connecting the two.

I knew my role in this *play* to the letter. I had only been called out by the family to get the old lady off the premises. Invariably, in spite of her violent protests, I ordered the old lady home on account of her blood pressure. I was always suitably rewarded by the happy looks on the faces of her children and a fee commensurate with the difficulty of my performance. The old lady of the dress shop and the owner of the fish and chip shop opposite were the best of friends! He did not wear her dresses and she vowed that she would never taste one of his chips until forced to do so in the condemned cell – waiting to be hanged!

Mr Kyprios, John's father-in-law, was most annoyed on looking out of his window at five in the morning, on the day John would most certainly return home. The undertakers on the other side of the road had gone too far! How dare they! The hearse which was always parked at night in the garage was now right outside his front door. Mr Kyprios was always up early. He went to Billingsgate fish market daily to buy his fish and he, like John, was not afraid of a hard day's work. This hearse however was too much! He was in a hurry to leave, too much of a hurry to leave a note of protest; he would certainly have something to say when the undertakers opened in the morning. Thank God he thought to himself as he took a quick glance at the hearse when passing they had not left a coffin in it.

As he drove towards Billingsgate, his mind alternating between fish and hearses, he suddenly became calm; he had solved the riddle of the hearse. The undertakers had obviously had to make an early start to collect a body for an early funeral and the hated vehicle would certainly not be there when he got back. He did not have to worry! He had solved the problem! He could now 'fish' without any qualms. He was feeling good.

He bought his fish and while the wholesaler was arranging for his fish to be loaded he went to join his friends at the local snack bar for a breakfast of bacon and eggs. This was one of the few occasions when he and his Greek friends could come together. They all worked in the fish and chip trade, all worked unsocial hours, all had their shops in different parts of London and apart from going to church their only recreation was work. Some who had grown-up sons in the trade were luckier, they could take an hour or two off at times.

Mr Kyprios, having eaten and drunk his fill and

exhausted the topics of conversation returned with his catch to the shop. He reached his home at 9.10 am, he was certain of the time for he checked his watch. It had never let him down in the thirty years he had owned it. Now, he really was going to *blow his top*! The hearse in all its glory was still there. He went to have a look. Horror of horrors, there was a body wrapped in a sheet on the floor of the hearse. There was however something not quite right! There was definitely a body on the floor of the hearse, but what was a blanket doing over the body?

He had heard of bodies being buried in a sheet, it was the normal custom in some countries of the Middle East, it was the first time however he had heard of a blanket. Still, the English were a peculiar race. It would not stretch one's imagination too far to imagine that someone had given an order to take a blanket with him. They would certainly believe they were going to a climate similar to their own! They would never for one moment believe that a country which had built an empire could possibly have one of its citizens sent down to the heat below.

He remembered quite well having had a chat one day in his shop with an Englishman who had booked himself a plot for his funeral at the undertakers opposite. The chap had been sincere; he had been quite firm in his instructions to the officials who were going to intern him. He did not believe in cremation, he was going to meet his maker face to face! The cemetery gates had to face east and his plot had to be on a hill. There was no way this chap was going to be buried in the lower slopes, they got waterlogged, and he suffered from rheumatism. He did not want to spend eternity in agonising pain from his joints!

Mr Kyprios crossed the road and went into the undertakers but there did not appear to be anyone minding the shop. He looked around him. He could see flowers on all sides and he could hear voices. He rang a bell placed on the counter, but no one appeared. He went to the door from which he heard the voices. He knocked. No one answered. This was too much! He was not going to be messed about. They had obviously heard him come in, knew who it was, and were purposely trying to avoid him. He was, by this time, in a blazing temper! He opened the door, went in, and came out in double-quick time. The room was full of naked bodies. A couple appeared to be placed on slabs, the rest were on trestle tables. He did not bother to count or take a second look. He crossed himself several times behind the closed door and fled the shop.

Mr Kyprios's tormentors had almost certainly come to give him a living death! They had found out his weakness, his Achilles heel, and were preparing to torture him. He went back to his home over the shop, poured himself out a couple of *arracks* which he swallowed quickly and looked out of his front window. The hearse was still there. The *arrack* however had certainly affected his brain, the body which he had previously seen wrapped up in a sheet was sitting up!

He poured himself out another drink and went to have another look, this time in very furtive fashion. He slowly pulled the curtains aside. He was going mad! The body had disappeared from the hearse! The back door of the vehicle was open and a white figure was standing up at the open door – yawning. Through the haze of the half-bottle of *arrack* which he had hastily consumed he thought he could recognise the figure. Before he could put a name to the body, it closed the back doors of the hearse, got into the driver's seat, and drove off.

Now Mr Kyprios was a superstitious and religious man, he had been so all his life; stupid he was not. Even though he had drunk far more *arrack* than was good for him he was not so inebriated as to alter his beliefs. He did not believe in the supernatural. There was no room for ghosts in his order of things. He simply did not believe in them. If he did not believe in them they did not exist. He could have sworn however that the silhouette at the back door of the hearse had all the characteristics of a man he had once seen with his son-in-law, John Hampton. He poured himself another *arrack*, then went into the kitchen to make himself a strong Turkish coffee to drink with it. There, sitting at the table as large-as-life was his son-in-law, and sitting opposite him, in animated conversation, was his daughter, Lisa!

The fish and chip shop did not open until 11.30 in the morning, and as it did not close until 11.00 at night, his wife who had worked late the previous night was still not up. She had a hard life looking after a family in cramped-living conditions over the shop especially when added to her duties as a housewife when her husband was not available she had to mind the shop. The previous day had been an exceptionally busy one and this is why Mr

Kyprios, as he sat down on a chair in the kitchen, was without his spouse.

John was apologising to his daughter for being so late in getting back, but the car he had bought, a hearse, which had been described in the catalogue as a transit van, was a *snip*! He had driven it from Exeter to Basingstoke without a hint of trouble, then, without warning, the engine had cut out. He had been stuck at the end of a road for an hour waiting for a breakdown truck to tow him to a garage: the problem had been dirty sparking plugs.

Mr Kyprios just sat there in a daze. He had never been a heavy drinker, never at least at 9.30 in the morning and his head was throbbing. He could hear John speaking to his daughter Lisa, but nothing of the conversation appeared to be registering in his brain. Suddenly, John turned to Lisa,

'Is there anything the matter with dad?'

Poor dad was now slouched at the table, moaning. His head ached from the amount of alcohol which he had drunk and moaning was a natural thing for him to do on an occasion such as this. Mr Kyprios looked at John.

'There was a hearse outside the shop all night. It is going to bring us bad luck!' he said.

John burst out laughing.

'The hearse! I bought it for sixty pounds in Exeter at an auction. Henry, my pal from Lewisham, has driven it back down here for me. After we broke down, I hired a car from a garage in case we broke down again and needed a tow. He left in the hearse much before me, the *blasted thing* is supposed to be a slow vehicle. What a joke! The hearse must have gone like a bomb with its new plugs! I told him to leave it outside the shop until I got home and if by any chance I was not back here by 9.30 this morning to park it in Consort Road and come back here with the keys. I told him you would go mad if you found a hearse outside the shop when you opened up. I can hear the door bell. It must be Henry.'

A fresh, young-looking, stubbly-faced Henry, now appeared in front of Mr Kyprios to shake his hand. Henry had apparently been able to get a few hours sleep on the floor of the hearse. He had not been disturbed by a single caller. No one, no one at all appeared to want to open the door of the hearse to see what lay inside! Henry had only one moan.

There had been no facilities for him to have a wash and shave in the 'blasted thing!'

6

Drink and Drugs

Gregory was a forty-five-year-old bachelor, a tall, balding, red-faced fellow, and the only time in the year I ever saw him was in the Christmas period. He was such a good patient, demanded so little of my time, I regarded myself lucky in having such a patient. I wished I had many more like him. After all, I was being paid by the National Health Service a yearly sum for the privilege of caring for him. In the fifties and sixties a National Health doctor was paid a basic allowance quarterly for each patient on his list. There were no hidden extras. Today, to reach the same sum which made up the allowance, extra work such as running an asthma clinic, a diabetic clinic, and deprivation allowances have to be taken into the calculation. Whereas in the early years of the health service the amount which a general practitioner earned could be worked out in minutes, now, an army of bureaucrats sweat day and night to calculate his or her income. Gregory would not have been such a profitable patient in today's NHS for he was not the type to pay much attention to preventive medicine.

Once a year, on the day after Boxing Day,

Gregory's landlady – he lived in a bedsitter in Holly Grove – would ask me to call and visit her lodger. The first time was in 1961, and the story in the following years was always the same. Gregory, her lodger, was semiconscious and doubled-up with pains in his stomach. She had gone into his room as she had not seen him about the house since Christmas Eve, and she had found her poor lodger lying in his bed, groaning. Even while she had been talking to him, asking him what the trouble was, he had been too busy vomiting to give her the time for a proper answer. She was sure the poor fellow was dying, would I please come as quickly as possible.

I would invariably be at the house within ten minutes and find him lying in bed in a pool of sweat, semicomatose and incoherent. I learned from his landlady, Gregory had returned from work on Christmas Eve at about five o'clock in the evening and had gone to see her with a box of chocolates to wish her a Happy Christmas. Christmas Day and Boxing Day she spent at her son's house in Belvedere, so she had no more contact with Gregory until she returned home and found him semiconscious: she had then immediately run around the corner for me. When I arrived, I found the room which reeked of alcohol full of empty bottles. The few bottles which contained a little liquid were scattered around the room as if they had been discarded because of their taste. I always managed to sober him up and he recovered; heaven only knows how! The history which my patient gave me when sober was, he had gone straight into his room on Christmas Eve and taken to the bottle. He had remained drunk, until rescued by his landlady.

Gregory had been born in India to an army couple, he had been an only child, and both parents had long since departed this life before Gregory had taken up residence in *leafy Peckham*. He had been educated in a private boarding school in Hampshire while his parents had been in India and he had remained in this country after completing his education. Because of his parents long service in the East they had lost all contact with any family, he did not even know whether he had any family left in this country. His landlady too was not of much help. All she was able to tell me about her lodger was, he went out to work every weekday, paid his rent regularly and punctually, and spent the whole of the Christmas period in his room drinking alone, until he became unconscious. After a couple of visits to his room on the day after Boxing Day, and once on the following day, he would be fit enough to come to see me at the surgery. He would then sit impassively in a chair while I would warn him off the devil drink. During my admonition he would look into my eyes as if I was reading a page of the Gospel then, without blinking an eyelid, after he thought I had finished preaching, ask me for a private certificate enabling him to return to work. I would sign one and give it to him: the charge would be the princely-sum of two shillings. I can still see him sitting in my consulting room as I described to him my experience in the army in Neumünster, Germany, in 1948. I did this to frighten him, but from the look on his face as I detailed my story I realised that I was fighting a lost cause: my story to him was a fairy tale.

I had been called to the sergeants mess, on Boxing Day, to treat a sergeant who had collapsed, and when I arrived I found the fellow lying on the floor – lifeless. The sergeant had been playing cards with some friends and had had the misfortune of winning every time. The card school had been playing not for money but for drinks and this sergeant had just won that one *hand* too many! Alcohol was very cheap in the sergeants mess, this fellow had been drinking gin: it is not too hard to imagine that it had not taken too many winning hands for the alcohol to do its dirty deed. The poor fellow had died of acute alcohol poisoning.

Gregory agreed with me that it was the most foolish thing to do to drink oneself unconscious and risk killing oneself. He would never do it again. He didn't, until the next year. He only ever needed two days to recover completely, his liver must have been *ox-like*! He really was a very fit man and my warnings therefore fell on deaf ears. I now cannot remember whether he ever told me what work he did, but his place of work must have been some benevolent institution to allow this yearly absence after a holiday to take place without remonstration.

I always forgot Gregory's existence until the following year when the same series of events would be repeated. This happened annually for eight years. In the ninth year however he complained of severe stomach pain after his yearly bout and as the pain was not relieved by the usual antacid treatment I referred him to hospital for investigation. He actually came to see me several times after this yearly bout as barium meal and X-ray examinations had revealed that the drink had finally got to him. It had benefited him with a large duodenal ulcer. I treated this successfully and warned him off drink, this he faithfully promised to do. I asked him to come for regular checkups, this unfortunately he failed to do. To be perfectly honest, his symptoms had been relieved, he felt well, he probably thought he was wasting both his and my time by coming back to see me. I had cured him, why bother to report a cure.

In 1971, ten years after his first attack, on the day after Boxing Day, I was called as usual by his landlady: this time however she appeared more anxious than usual. She told me that not hearing any movements, not even moans and groans coming from Gregory's room, she had taken the liberty of going to his bed. He was cold. As she appeared to be distressed, I accompanied her home and found Gregory's room in its usual post-Christmas disarray, with gin, whisky and sherry bottles littered all over the place. The smell of alcohol was overpowering! I actually felt dizzy while trying to examine the fellow for signs of life.

I had however on this occasion come too late. He had just had that drop too much. His ulcer had burst! The *spirits* had spirited him away.

*   *   *

Fashions have not changed, women who now restrict themselves to a daily consumption of food

180

which equates them with the daily diet of a rabbit behaved in a similar fashion in the sixties. The problem we had then, it was not known that amphetamines and its derivatives were so habit forming and that their addiction caused so many mental changes. The war of 1939-45 was still fresh in people's minds and benzedrine had been a stable diet for many of us to keep awake. No self-respecting pilot on a bombing mission which would have meant him being in the air for untold hours would have dared to go without a handful of benzedrine tablets in his pocket. The advantage of taking these stimulants, apart from the natural one of preventing sleep was that they also decreased a person's appetite for food. Indeed, as many of us who had need to take these tablets recognised, they removed the need for food completely if none was available. Paradoxically, as the need for food decreased, the need for a cigarette increased!

Dexedrine (dexamphetamine sulphate), one of the benzedrine derivatives, I used extensively in the fifties for its appetite-suppressant properties without any worries. Mrs Pike, who came on to my list because her doctor would not listen to her pleadings for weight-reduction therapy, was monitored by me monthly for her obesity and was prescribed dexedrine tablets. She was therefore a regular attender at my surgery. Her children at the time had not yet been on my list long enough to drive me mad with their many complaints. I had not yet seen enough of them to wish that I had entered another profession – the veterinary one – where the troublesome patient can be put down! Not having any experience of dealing with this family I found it unusual in 1959 for the good lady to come in to see me daily with her son Peter, suffering from a sore throat. When one looked at him he did not appear at all ill, but complained bitterly of not being able to swallow and what was worse, as time passed, he did not appear to be improving on my treatment.

After I had been treating him for two whole weeks for tonsillitis, when instead of getting better he appeared to be getting steadily worse, even I began to become a little concerned. Peter was wasting away before our eyes, though the only two symptoms he complained of were a sore throat and a raging thirst. My main remedy for children with a sore throat was to advise the mother to buy ice cream, I was now in the process of bankrupting the Pikes!

With no improvement in Peter's condition and her rapidly depleting housekeeping budget, it was no surprise mom was becoming very anxious. As Peter was able to get about and had no temperature I believed at first that he must have diabetes and insisted that mom bring me in twice daily specimens of the boy's urine for testing. Although she brought me in six samples over three days as requested, there was never a trace of sugar to be found. All my own investigations had now led me up a blind alley and as I could not tell mom when her son would return to his normal obnoxious self, I became more than a little concerned. I found myself in the difficult position of pronouncing Peter not to be ill, yet could not say he was well. And although I had been treating him with penicillin for two weeks, he was still showing no signs of improvement. Penicillin by mouth does have some funny side effects, one of them is a dry mouth; in the belief the treatment itself might be causing symptoms I stopped it. Still no improvement!

In normal circumstances I would have asked for a second opinion, in this case however there had not been any reason to seek one. Peter had not really been ill enough in the classical sense. Now, when Mrs Pike brought him in to see me on the sixteenth day of his illness the boy was twitching and hyperactive and Mrs Pike told me that Peter had not been able to sleep for two whole nights. He also now appeared to be showing signs of dehydration. I was baffled. Mrs Pike was demoralised. I suggested to Mrs Pike that she should take Peter into one of the hospital casualty departments, but she then shamefacedly admitted to me she had already done so. On successive days, she had taken the boy to the casualty departments of King's College Hospital, Dulwich Hospital and St Giles Hospital, and had been told on each occasion by the casualty officer who had examined Peter to continue with the treatment I had prescribed for him. I now had to use my *spiel*.

'Only a specialist can now save the lad,' I said.

I would give her a letter to the Ear Nose and Throat consultant, at King's College Hospital, a chap I knew personally, there would be no problem, and he would see young Peter that same day. Before giving her the letter, not wishing to appear a fool before the students who would be accompanying the hospital consultant and reading my letter, I tried to make a diagnosis. I examined the boy thoroughly again from head to toe. I remained as wise at the end of the examination as at the beginning.

I sat down at my desk to write my letter to the consultant, with Peter all of eight years old, standing by my side prompting me as to the exact nature of his symptoms and how my treatment had affected him. I suddenly stopped writing in the middle of a sentence. Peter would just not allow me to concentrate. He would not stop talking, but his babbling now forced me to apply brakes to my pen. He was nonchalantly informing me that he was still taking medication. I looked at my notes, they confirmed that he had only been prescribed enough for two courses and each course should have lasted five days.

'According to my reckoning you should have stopped taking medicine about five days ago,' I said.

'You mean the horrible, thick, white stuff you gave me, well I did!'

'But you have just told me that you are still taking medicine for your throat,' I persisted.

'I'm not taking the filthy horrible medicine. I am just sucking the lozenges and they taste awful,' was his answer.

I could not believe him. I had prescribed penicillin medicine on two occasions, lozenges only once, then only twenty. There was no way that twenty pleasant-tasting lozenges could have been made to last sixteen days by a boy with a sweet tooth.

With my face only inches away from this gaunt rascal, I now asked him to explain how he had managed to suck nonexistent lozenges. To my horror, I discovered that he had been sucking his mother's dexedrine tablets which I had prescribed for her obesity. When his own lozenges had run out Peter had gone to his mother's bedside cupboard and helped himself to hers!

Mrs Pike was overcome with embarrassment and began to reprimand the young lad. The family had only been my patients for a short time and she was shocked at being proved negligent. Peter was however not lost for an answer. He had, when I had been attempting to write a letter at his dictation been looking at me, now that I had stopped his interest in me had evaporated. He turned to his mother and in a high-pitched voice blurted out,

'I don't know why you bothered to change to this doctor mom, I tell you his medicine is awful! Even the lozenges he gives you taste horrible.'

How I kept my hands off the lad I will never know, but I am glad I did. The fellow remained on my list until at the tender age of forty-eight – without any history of heart disease – on a camping holiday with his family, he had a heart attack. He was found dead under a caravan while trying to fix a wheel.

* * *

It was two o'clock in the morning, in May 1956 – we still lived on the surgery premises – when I was awakened by the frantic ringing of the front door bell followed by repeated loud knocking on the front door. I jumped out of bed, put on a pair of trousers and dressing gown, and fled down the stairs to open the front door. I was not so disturbed at the frantic knocking as I was scared that the noise might have already awakened my youngster who was only six years old: once awake, he would almost certainly have kept me up the rest of the night playing with him.

When I opened the front door I found standing on the doorstep a soldier in uniform, who asked me quite politely to follow him: he had just seen a corpse lying in the road! I grabbed my medical case and did as he asked. Indeed, there was a corpse, a rather corpulent one, lying in the road between two cars outside the Prince Albert public house, snoring heavily. The street lamp on the corner illuminated his appearance so well that I found it hard to understand how the soldier could have believed the man to have been a dead body. His chest heaved with every breath and his snoring could not only be heard, it was so loud, it seemed to cause the cars on either side of his body to vibrate. The *stiff* was a man in evening dress, an obese chap, with a red and bloated face and a chin covered in blood. I later ascertained this blood was from a laceration on his forehead, the blood had trickled down his face to his chin.

It only took me two seconds to determine the fact that this man had not ended up between two cars by being knocked down. The smell of alcohol exhaled at every breath gave me the diagnosis. This fellow, dead drunk, had obviously at some time of the night staggered out of the pub and lost his balance. He had fallen down and cut his head on one of the projections of a car in his fall. Once down he had stayed down. He had been too drunk to get up! The only question which caused me a little disquiet, what was he doing at that time in the morning lying there when the pubs had been closed some hours earlier?

I examined the fellow whilst he was still supine between the cars, I did not want to move him until I had made certain my diagnosis of drunkenness was accurate. It was! He reacted to my slapping, he moved his head about, and when I tried to open his eyes to test his conjunctival reflexes he resisted my attempts quite forcibly. My slapping of his face and undoing his shirt to examine his chest appeared to arouse him from his slumber. He tried to sit up and move his mouth, but it was too much for him. He slithered back between the cars to continue his snoring.

The soldier had stood by my side whilst I had gone through the motions of determining the cause of this man's accident and when I explained the casualty was not a *stiff*, he agreed to help me carry the fellow to my surgery – only a few yards away. It may only have been a matter of twenty yards, the chap however was a dead weight. Although we were both fit and healthy we were forced to rest for some minutes after our exertions.

We laid him on my examination couch where I sutured the laceration on his forehead. Now I was grateful he had anaesthetized himself by his own efforts with the amount of alcohol he had consumed. The amount of movement made by the patient was minimal and I managed to carry out the whole operation without any extra-medication. I am sure that he did not feel a thing. He certainly later had no recollection of my surgical accomplishments.

I was lucky, the whole exercise was carried out without waking any of my household, everyone remained asleep. The soldier and I even managed to enjoy a couple of beers afterwards whilst we discussed what to do with our uninvited and unwelcome guest. Suddenly, without warning, our drunken friend decided his drunken state was no longer a bar to movement and he sat up on the couch. He tried to climb up, but failed. He sank back. The effort had proved just that little too much. It sent him back to sleep again and his snoring now sounded louder than ever.

There was no way I was prepared to spend the night nursing a drunken, snoring, miscreant, even if he did sport a smart suit and a bow tie. This act of movement on his part decided me to take some action and bring the *play* to a close. I made him a strong cup of tea, black as the ace of spades and the soldier forced his mouth open while I poured it down his throat praying that it was not going into his lungs and drowning him. My treatment worked. He revived sufficiently for me to determine that he had recovered enough from his carousing to call a cab to take him home.

The accident which had not been a very serious one turned out eventually to be a very profitable one for me. When the chap came back to have his sutures removed I discovered that he was a wealthy accountant, a partner in a city firm, and the boyfriend of the lady publican who was the licensee of the Prince Albert. He was a married man with a wife and children in Hastings: he also had a 'pad' in Soho.

He told me the story of the eventful night while he was having his stitches removed. As he had already intimated to me that he was an asthmatic and wanted to be a private patient I was a willing listener. The lady publican, he told me proudly, was his mistress. On the fateful night they had quarrelled, she had become maniacal and had physically thrown him into the street. His description of the altercation had to be truthful, he was a twenty-stone man and I knew the lady. She must indeed have been in a mad rage, she could not have weighed more than nine stone!

The cold night air, the way he had been transported into the street, the amount of whisky he had drunk had all combined to poleaxe him: in attempting to get into his car he had staggered and fallen on to the car behind. He did not remember anything more until he had found himself fully dressed, lying on a settee in his flat in Soho, at seven o'clock that Saturday morning. He did not know how he had sustained the laceration and the only reason he had now come to see me was that his ladylove had watched a soldier, with my help, cart his body away. She had rightly assumed that he had been taken to my surgery, more than this he could not tell me.

As he did not live in the area and his National Health doctor was in Hastings, I had no guilt whatsoever in accepting him as a private patient. I treated him for some years, until his ladyfriend retired from the trade and left the area. Some years later, I learned from a friend of his ladyfriend, not only had the lady left the trade, but she had left him too, for pastures new.

7

Behaviour Problems

Morals have changed so much since I entered general practice many thousands of books have been written on the subject. The girl who would have said NO in 1953, and meant it, is not now given the opportunity to use the same reasons. Sex, is now regarded by most youngsters as just an extension of the kiss and as long as the male partner wears a condom no harm is done. Virginity has become the exclusive right of the religious girl. The obvious concern of the young girl not to become pregnant, the natural instinct of a young man not to put his girlfriend in the family way, was the reason for the paucity of sexual activity before the appearance of the contraceptive pill. After all, if the fellow was so unlucky as to give her a baby he had to marry the girl, whether he loved her or not. The girl's father would have killed him otherwise. A single parent was regarded as an outcast by society and as little help as possible was given to the unfortunate girl. Her life was effectively ruined!

Marcia Clay, was brought to see me in May 1963 by her mother, because Marcia was steadily putting on weight and her clothes no longer fitted her.

Marcia, nineteen years old, had always been a little plump, but nothing like the barrel she was now. Her mother's request was specific. Would I please put Marcia on a slimming diet and give her some slimming pills. I was not going to argue with Mrs Clay who was, to put it mildly, a lady who knew her own mind. I did however have enough courage to make one proviso, I would only be prepared to do as she asked after I had examined the girl. She agreed to my suggestion and Marcia was unceremoniously ordered by mom to lie on my couch and expose her abdomen. After I had examined Marcia's belly, was convinced in my own mind the girl was five months pregnant and suggested to the mother in order to make a firm diagnosis I should do an internal examination I thought mom would have an apoplectic fit!

'Don't you know Marcia is a virgin? I always understood you could not examine a virgin! What have you found wrong with her stomach?' she shrieked.

'There is something definitely wrong with Marcia's abdomen for her to have a lump the size of a football in her pelvis,' was my stammered, frightened reply.

'I know what that is due to,' Mrs Clay answered.

'Marcia helped her dad pick up a piano two months ago: she has strained muscles in her stomach'.

'When did Marcia last have a period?' I asked.

'How should I know? I would not be surprised if she is on now!' was the answer.

Whilst Marcia's mother and I had enjoyed our

ding-dong battle, Marcia had been a passive onlooker: one would have thought she was an imbecile who could not answer for herself. In fact, Marcia was a very attractive, intelligent, young lady, who thought it wise in the circumstances to leave all the answers to her mom.

I was at the time, a forty-year-old general practitioner, with a good deal of experience, but Mrs Clay was a formidable fifty-eight-year-old cockney, who had produced nine other Clays besides Marcia: Marcia was her youngest. I was no match for Mrs Clay! I now just did not know how to continue this conversation. Whatever I now said I was going to be contradicted and made to look foolish. In my make-up there is an element of cowardice, I like to call it discretion. I am perfectly happy to admit however that on this occasion it was pure and simple cowardice. If I had not been a coward I would not have taken the coward's way out. I would have stuck to my guns and told Mrs Clay that whatever her diagnosis, it was the wrong one. Like it or not, Marcia was five months pregnant. The coward part in my nature however rebelled against my taking on Mrs Clay, and sublimated any attempt of bravery. It prevailed!

'It is possible Marcia's lump could possibly be due to a fibroid and in the circumstances, as it would be dangerous to give her slimming pills, I am going to refer her to the gynaecological consultant at King's College Hospital', I said.

My statement Marcia might possibly have a fibroid did the trick: it deflated Mrs Clay. She agreed that in the circumstances it would be best to have her daughter referred to a gynaecological specialist and I referred her to Mr Clayton, one of my old teachers, at King's College Hospital. My letter to him, and his reply to me, are things which one does not forget even after thirty-two years.

Dear Mr Clayton,

> My young nineteen-year-old patient, Marcia Clay, was brought in to see me by her mother as she has become obese. On examination, there is no doubt in my mind that this girl is twenty-weeks pregnant. Her mother however insists that this girl is a virgin and the lump in her pelvis is due to her picking up a piano! I believe the tune which was played on this girl was not one of which her mother would have approved. I would be very grateful if you would see her and for your opinion.

His reply was unusual in that after he had seen Marcia I had a reply on the following day. Replies from hospital usually did not arrive for several weeks, sometimes not at all, and I must add even today things have not changed all that much. Obviously, Mr Clayton had enjoyed the consultation with the forthright mother as much as I had done. His letter was as follows.

Dear Dr Crown,

> Thank you for your letter. I have examined Miss Clay and had a

consultation with her mother. I would like to point out that the patient's mother is both right and wrong. The girl is definitely not a virgin! This is where mother is wrong. She is however right when she attributes her daughter's condition to picking up a piano. What she forgot to mention to you however is that Piano happens to be the surname of the man she picked up! I have booked her for full antenatal care in the hospital.

Marcia, now diagnosed as pregnant by the hospital consultant, had no further cause to hide her embarrassment and came to see me immediately after I had received the hospital letter to explain the reason for her fall from grace.

She worked as a typist in a city firm and the office in which she worked – there were twenty on the staff roll – always held its Christmas party on its premises. With too much drink inside her on the night of the party, she had allowed her boss inside her as well. Her problem was, when she found out that she was pregnant, she could not definitely prove the boss was the father of her baby. She had been so paralytic drunk, it could easily have been any of the other seven men at the party who had given her the present.

Every man at the party was married. When she had approached them, each one was aghast at even being asked as to whether they could possibly have

195

been responsible for taking away her virginity. She was now in a predicament. There was no way her father would allow her to remain at home with a fatherless baby. Her father was an old-fashioned type who, if he found she was pregnant would regard her as a fallen woman and not worthy to be regarded by him as his daughter. She was going to be cast out on the streets. Could I now please help. She had heard that there was a Mother and Baby home where a girl could be admitted for confinement and then have the baby adopted. A friend of hers had been in the same predicament and her doctor had helped her, could I now please give her a letter of referral to the home.

I suddenly had a brainwave. I knew a fellow from whom I had bought a television set, a young man in his thirties, married and childless, who had often come to see me for advice. The couple had spent an enormous amount of money in gynaecological infertility clinics for investigations to be finally told that there was no hope of them ever producing a baby. He was quite a wealthy chap, we had spoken on several occasions about adoption, but the problem was, there was such a long waiting list of couples seeking to adopt a baby. I now had the solution to one couple's problem.

I arranged for Mrs Clay and her daughter to meet the Pattersons – the childless couple – and the Pattersons took the pair to their home in Surrey, in the stockbroker belt, to show them what kind of a home and what kind of an upbringing their offspring was going to inherit. The Clays were overcome. The house was luxurious. As Marcia herself told me, her baby was going to a home with all the comforts which her family could not have provided in a hundred years. There had been one snag when they had visited. The Pattersons had a dog who had immediately taken a dislike to Mrs Clay. He obviously did not like women not dressed in the height of fashion. To prove his point, he had grabbed hold of her skirt as she passed him and attempted to drag it off. She had naturally resisted and he had then taken a bite at her bottom. Presumably, the flesh from the poorer classes was not to his taste. He had run off as if infected by the plague, barking like mad. This, I persuaded the Clays was not going to be his behaviour towards the grandchild. The child was going to be brought up in a family with *blue blood* and no self-respecting dog attacks the flesh of a person who is brought up in this environment.

Marcia had her confinement in Dulwich Hospital and the proviso between the parties made before the event took place was that Marcia was not to see the baby. The trauma of seeing it, perhaps even given it to hold, would have been too much for her to let it go for adoption. Marcia had told me in no uncertain terms that she really wanted to keep the baby and should she be given it to hold she would never be parted from it. She loved children and her only aspiration in life was to get married and have loads of *kids*. The only reason she was allowing the present adoption to take place was to prevent her father from ever finding out she was pregnant.

All went well. She had an uncomplicated delivery and produced a healthy seven-and-half pound girl.

The baby was taken away as soon as the umbilical cord was cut then transferred into the care of the Pattersons. Marcia never saw the baby. Although she had some depression after its birth which I regarded as a perfectly natural event, she recovered completely.

In 1968, when Marcia was twenty-four-years old, she came into my surgery one evening to ask me to do her a favour. She was so shy in putting her request I immediately thought it was something to do with her childbirth and I was right. She had met a chap whom she was going to marry and as she would be leaving the area she did not want her future husband to know anything of her previous pregnancy. She had told him she was a virgin and as the couple had no intention of having sex before marriage she did not want him to find out anything of her past history.

'What the devil are you talking about! I have never heard such nonsense! As far as I know you are a virgin,' I replied.

I watched the happy smile on her face as I scrubbed out all the references of her previous pregnancy in my notes and gave her all the hospital reports concerning her pregnancy and confinement to tear up. I can still remember the contented face as she deposited the shreds of paper in my wastepaper basket. Perhaps, in hindsight, I was not behaving ethically. I did not care, in my opinion I was saving her life.

Marcia married the fellow of her dreams and went to live in the Midlands. I have not seen her now for over fifteen years, ever since she came down to London to attend her mother's funeral and popped in to see me to tell me that she had three *kids*. Her appearance gave me great satisfaction. I had been the intermediary in providing an unwanted baby to a couple who desperately wanted one, also to a couple who had the means of providing this baby with all the love and comfort which money could buy.

The Pattersons indeed worshipped their adopted daughter and although not patients of mine, they sent me photographs of her at odd times, to show me how happy and contented the child was in their care. The photographs always made me envious of the toys which they were able to provide for her and which I could never have afforded for my own children. What I did not know until much later was, the Pattersons had pretended to all their friends and relatives that Mrs Patterson had been the natural mother and had prepared them for the event with fictitious stories.

The television shop had long closed down, I had not been in touch with the family for some years, when I received a strongly-worded letter from Croydon Borough Council, asking me to explain my reasons for breaking the law. I was warned that I could be fined heavily for my action, even receive a custodial sentence. I had contravened sections X, Y, Z, of some law on adoption. I can't remember the exact terminology, but this letter frightened me out of my wits. Evidently, the Pattersons – before I had been in touch with them – had had their names registered with several adoption agencies and when one of the agencies had finally, after several years, offered them a backward child to adopt, they had refused. They had replied that they had adopted a baby from a private source and were certainly not interested in adopting a backward one. The agency had reported the matter to the social services who, finding no record in their files, had written to the Pattersons for the name of the agency who had arranged the adoption; the perpetrator of the crime. It was me! I had broken the law! Before going to prison and being crossed off the medical list, would I please explain myself! I was so overwrought at the time, had the case gone to court I would have been perfectly justified in pleading insanity.

My letter in reply to the social services, although strictly honest, would have taken a prize in humbleness and grovelling, if a prize were given in these subjects. It only stopped at being prepared to lick their boots. I explained that I had not known they should have been informed at the time and added, the baby had been transferred directly from the midwifery department of Dulwich Hospital into the care of the Pattersons. Whilst I was quite prepared to give them the name and address of the Pattersons, I was not, in any circumstances, prepared to divulge the name or address of the mother. She had since the unfortunate episode married a fellow who knew nothing of her past medical history and I was not prepared to risk ruining her life.

Authority sometimes does appear to have a heart. After visiting the Pattersons' home, the social services sent me a glowing letter of praise for my behaviour in being able to find such a loving home for a child. They did however warn me not to repeat my action and the consequences which would follow should I do so. They also found it possible to persuade themselves to send me three forms to be completed in duplicate relating to the adoption. As the adoption had taken place some years previously, this was obviously done to tax my memory and give me aggravation!

If you, dear reader, recognise yourself as one of the characters in this story, I still remember you with affection and send you my warmest felicitations.

*　　*　　*

Martin had no Jewish connections. He was a forty-year-old dock worker, his father had been a dock worker, his grandfather too had worked in the docks all his life, and as far as he could remember his forbears had worked in or around the docks all their lives. You had to have a union card to work in the docks in 1955, the card was handed down from generation to generation, it was a closed shop, and it was kept in the family. Martin's work was a backbreaking one, but he made a good living. Although he was searched every night on leaving his work there were ways and means of *working a fiddle*.

He and his wife lived in a council flat at the junction of the New and Old Kent Roads, where the new flyover has bypassed them and placed their block in one of the side roads. When Martin first registered with me he had been single and lived in Talfourd Road, but when he married and moved to his new address I did not have a large enough list of patients to be able to afford to tell him to change to another practice nearer to him. After all, there were very few cars about in the fifties; in an emergency, it would have only have taken me a few minutes to get to his new address.

Martin's wife, Freda, had suffered from gynaecological problems since puberty and had registered with me immediately after their marriage. She was a twenty-five-year-old serious woman, who had suffered her symptoms stoically. By the time this story of Martin's life about which I am writing began she had already been a frequent attender at my surgery – we had become friends. Martin himself had been on the list of my predecessor, he had been one of the two-hundred patients on Dr Morgan's list who had been left for me to commence a career in Peckham. I had inherited him. I had never had to treat him before my first call out and only knew him by reputation. What I found strange, Martin's wife at times discussed her husband to me and mentioned that he had allergic problems. I could not understand it: I could offer no treatment: I had never come across the complaint before and it was not in any of the medical text books. He was allergic to antisemitism!

Martin was fond of his daily tipple in the local pub and was quite happy in filling his belly with beer every night to come home jolly and merry. There were occasions however when he came home bruised and battered having been involved in a fight. He would never tell her the cause of the fight, except to say that a *bloke* had been rude to him and he had retaliated. A fight had broken out: she could see for herself that he was not seriously hurt: why worry? These fights however were something which Freda just could not understand, her husband was a meek and mild man. When she felt peeved – in the house she was the boss – and persisted in her enquiries as to the cause of a fight, he shut up like a clam.

One night, he came home with a gashed face, someone had used a broken bottle on her husband and he had been to casualty at St Giles Hospital for the laceration to be sutured. This now was something new, and she was not prepared to allow this to pass without investigation. As Martin would not tell her, she went to see the landlord of the pub to ask him for an explanation as to how the accident had occurred. He told Freda he was as puzzled as she was. Had she not come to see him, he had intended to come and see her himself and ask what kind of a man her husband was. His description of the previous night's events was precise in every detail.

Martin had been drinking happily with two of his mates at 10.00 o'clock the previous night at the bar when some strangers – the landlord had never seen them before – entered the public bar and asked for pints of beer. The strangers sat down at one of the tables near the bar and the landlord could overhear the conversation to the exact word. It was something to do with buying suits. One the men had said, 'you should have your head examined, you should have expected an f...... Jew bastard to fiddle you like that!'

They had been speaking amongst themselves. Martin had not been a party to their conversation at any point. Their conversation however had evidently been loud enough for Martin to overhear. Martin had gone berserk! He left the bar, ran to the chap who had made the remark, and allowed his right fist with all his weight behind it land on the fellow's nose. Martin's action had been so unexpected the fellow had not been able to defend himself. The man who had made the remark had been knocked to the ground and it was only natural his friends had retaliated. They had rushed at Martin, knocked him down, one of them had then used a bottle on Martin's face. It was really lucky Martin's friends had been with him in the pub, they had dragged Martin away, they had rescued him from a real beating.

He couldn't understand it! Whenever the subject of Jews was brought up Martin became aggressive. He knew Martin's friends avoided mentioning Jews, good or bad, in his presence, but for the life of him did not know why. It was funny really, the landlord knew Martin's father and grandfather. His family had always lived in Deptford and he had gone to the same school as Martin. He could swear there was no Jewish blood in Martin's family. He had however noticed Martin's character had changed since his return from the Forces. The years spent as a prisoner of war in Germany had definitely altered Martin: he had certainly been a different chap before he joined the merchant navy. He attributed the change to the fact Martin's ship had been torpedoed and he had been taken prisoner so early in the war. The war had only just begun, it was early 1940, and Martin was already out of it. Martin had never been able to fire a shot in anger! Martin's hatred of Germans it was possible to understand, but this Jewish aspect beat him.

He himself had no connection with Jews and he could not remember when he had last seen one. As far as he could recollect there were no Jewish boys in the school which they had attended in Deptford. The only Jew Freda herself had consciously known to be one was me and she had had no idea until her conversation with the landlord that there had been any association between Martin's outbreaks of aggression and Jews. His previous injuries had never been severe enough to warrant any medical interference and it was quite by accident that I eventually became involved.

The sutures in Martin's face had been removed in the casualty department of St Giles Hospital and I had played no part in this little escapade of his. The episode of *bottle scraping* had taken place in 1955, my involvement in Martin's personal life however did not take place until a year later.

It was a very dark afternoon, in February 1956, when Freda telephoned from a neighbour's flat that Martin had been brought home from the docks by his mates, feeling unwell. He was boiling hot, complained of a sore throat, was having difficulty in swallowing, and what was most unusual for a man with Martin's temperament had taken to his bed.

Could I please call and see him. After evening surgery would do.

It was already four o'clock, and I honestly did not feel like going out into the rush-hour traffic in the Old Kent Road at that particular time. I was tired. I had been up most of the night on a maternity case, so I promised Freda that I would call after surgery. Would she please sponge him down with tepid water until I arrived!

It was nine o'clock in the evening when I arrived at their flat and Freda who answered the door was delighted to see me. Martin, she told me, had taken a turn for the worse. He was delirious, kept shouting that he was freezing cold, and when you felt his body you could boil an egg on it. She did not have enough blankets in the house to keep him warm! When I went into the bedroom with her I found Martin was having an attack of rigors and was clutching a sheet tightly to his chest. His eyes were closed, he was shaking uncontrollably and it was difficult even to approach him. Trying to examine him was proving an impossible task for he would not allow me to unwind the sheet which he kept bound around him like an Egyptian mummy.

Serious examination below the neck however was superfluous, his neck was grossly swollen, even visual examination was enough to see the marked enlargement of his tonsillar and cervical glands. The diagnosis could never be in doubt – acute tonsillitis. Could it however be diphtheria? Now I had the task of asking, rather forcing a delirious man to open his mouth so that I could have a look at his throat. A wooden spatula would have been as much use as a jelly sandwich. I asked Freda for a metal tablespoon.

Martin and I struggled for a few seconds whilst I attempted to insert the spoon between his clenched teeth, when he suddenly opened his eyes. With open-wide, wild eyes, he looked straight into my face and flung himself upwards to grab me round the neck. He pulled me down with him on the bed.

'*Save me doc! Save me doc!*' he screamed. '*Thank God it's you! Save me doc!*'

He just as suddenly let me go and sank down on the bed. He opened his mouth without protest. I took a quick look at his grossly-swollen infected tonsils and began the task of saving him! I gave him an injection of a million units of soluble crystalline penicillin into the muscle of his upper left arm, ordered Freda not to feed him, to sponge him down with tepid water and to give him plenty of cold water to drink. I told her that I would call again in the morning before I commenced morning surgery to continue the process of saving her husband! He had after all insisted I do so!

In the morning, although Martin was a little better, he was still incoherent, still running a temperature, still toxic, so I gave him another injection of penicillin. I went again that evening after surgery and thankfully by this time the penicillin had done its work. He was much cooler, his temperature was only a little above normal, he still however had the glazed-look which is the hallmark of a patient whose blood chemistry is awry.

When I called on the following morning, the second day of his illness, the bed was empty. Martin, weak, dopey-looking, was sitting in an armchair in the dining room. When I asked him why he had reacted so violently on the first night of his illness replied,

'*have you got a brother doc?*' My answer was 'No! Why?'

'*Well, you've certainly got a double! You're the spitting image of a chap killed by the Germans.*'

I was intrigued. I asked him to tell me about it.

'Some other time. It's a long story. I am too weak now,' was the reply.

'I will come back again tonight to give you another *jab* and you can tell me then,' I said. He just nodded.

That evening, after giving him an injection, I sat down and waited. He realised as I had seated myself after the *jab* and Freda had kindly provided me with a cup of tea, from my positioning, this liquid was not going to be gulped down. There was also no way I had any intention of leaving until all was revealed. He now told me the story of his life as a merchant seaman.

He was twenty-three years old, in 1939, when he volunteered to join the Merchant Navy. Having worked in the docks, with a knowledge of ships, his services were accepted with alacrity. He did the American trips on a merchant ship which had the unfortunate experience in 1940 – on a trip from Newfoundland to Liverpool – of being torpedoed in mid-Atlantic. In the explosion Martin had suffered cuts and bruises, what was however much more serious he found that he could not put any weight on his left leg. When he felt down his leg he felt faint, it didn't feel right, there was a bulge in his thigh. Even trying to move it was excruciating. He found out afterwards that he had suffered a fractured femur. He now owed his life to his shipmates who, realising that he could not walk, physically manhandled him into a life raft at the risk of their own lives. To this day, he does not know whether these men who saved his life survived the war themselves. He was in agony in the raft and as he recounted his experiences remembered not caring whether he lived or died. In any event, he was convinced that he was going to die and the other men in the raft felt the same way too. It was only a matter of time.

After being in the raft for an eternity – this actually proved to be no more than eleven hours – they were astonished to see the conning tower of a submarine slowly emerge from the water a few yards from them. It was getting dark, and it was frightening to see the dark silhouette of a *U-boat* (submarine) which had probably been the cause of all their suffering slowly come into view.

A figure appeared on the *U-boat* and the men in the raft paddled towards him. They did not know or care what happened. They had just seen a live human being in the middle of the ocean. They would have been just as willing to welcome the devil for a drink of water to quench the thirst in their parched throats. As they looked, to their amazement, more men appeared on the deck of the submarine. These men lowered a boat and rowed to their raft. They then attached a rope to their raft and dragged it to the submarine. Martin and his mates in the raft were then hauled on board. Martin himself was manhandled from the raft in agonising pain and in the process of being transferred believes that he must have passed out. He remembers being hauled out of the raft, then nothing more until lying in a bunk and finding (ME) – my double – bending over him, giving him an injection.

My double he found out later was a Polish-Jewish doctor, who had been on his way from France to America, on a ship which had suffered the same fate as Martin's merchant ship. Why the Germans had kept the doctor on the boat, Martin never found out. Martin could not speak a word of Polish, the doctor could only speak a few words of faltering English, so the only communication between them was by sign language. In any event, Martin swears he owes his life to my double.

The doctor set his fracture as best as he could with walking sticks and a plank of wood, dressed his wounds, and kept an eye on him all the time he was on the boat. They were on the boat for about a month, until the *U-boat* returned to its base in Eckernförde, Germany.

Martin, by this time, could hobble a little on his broken leg, and was sent to a prisoner-of-war camp in Germany. After a period of convalescence of eight weeks in the camp, when his foot was in the experience of a German doctor fit to bear weight, he was put in a working party whose job it was to bury the dead of a concentration camp nearby. At the time, the British prisoners really believed this was a labour camp, they had no idea this was a *concentration camp*. To be honest, it was not until the war had ended they learned such camps actually existed and that their prisoner-of-war camp had been sited next to one. They believed that the prison next to their camp was where German criminals and other wrongdoers were sent to serve out their sentences. The only thing which puzzled their working party was, why the dead were so emaciated and why so many dead! The working party however did not really concern themselves over this aspect of their work. They were after all only doing what they hoped their army was doing – burying Germans! They had been taught the only good German was a dead one, why should they be upset at their work?

One day, Martin's heart missed a beat. He was throwing into a mass grave the man who had saved his life! He had not known the doctor had been in this camp, but presumed at the time he had been posted there as the prison doctor. This doctor, whose face had been imprinted in his memory, had been a podgy thirty-year-old man; now, although the face was still recognisable, the body was that of a skeleton. The chap had no marks on his body which would have meant torture or violence but was so emaciated Martin thought tuberculosis or some other disease must have been the cause of such extreme wasting.

Martin was released when the Germany army capitulated and on returning home found his union card allowing him to return to work in the docks had been retained by his family. He returned to work in the docks, but it was not long before the words concentration camps became everyday talk. It was then the part he had played in the disposal of the bodies hit him. He suddenly realised his Polish doctor friend – the man who had saved his life – had almost certainly been starved to death! For some reason, he felt guilty. He developed an obsession. Whenever anyone made an anti-semitic remark, the picture of this Polish-Jewish doctor appeared in front of him crying out for vengeance. His last statement summed up all his previous violent actions.

'I just can't help myself doc! An uncontrollable anger comes over me! I have to hit the bloke! *You're sure you've never had an older brother doc?'*

Martin and his wife left the area in the early sixties and emigrated to Australia. Apart from one picture postcard, which I received six months after they left this country and settled in Adelaide, I have not heard from them.

* * *

A car has always been just as much a part of a general practitioner's life as his stethoscope, his instruments, and his pen; without any one of them he cannot function properly. My very first car was a Standard 8, which I bought in 1950, when I took up the post of a trainee assistant to Dr Gordon, in Hendon. This car gave me serious cause for concern on three occasions, by threatening me, the lives of my passengers, and the lives of pedestrians passing by when my driving seat broke away from the base forcing me to control the car in the supine position. It was no joke when driving serenely along to be suddenly catapulted from the sitting to the lying-down position when one was supposed to be in control of the vehicle!

This car also had a novelty, it had a sunroof. A sunroof in a car in the early fifties was not exactly the same as one in the nineties: my sunroof not only allowed in the sun, it allowed in the rain too even when completely closed. I once sat mesmerised in a storm sitting in the driving seat – parked in the main street in Reading – watching my late father-in-law sitting in the passenger seat being soaked to the skin. The sunroof, tightly shut, was using him as a drain. He could not leave the car, there was a tropical downpour outside! Needless to say, I changed that car soon afterwards.

The Blackmores in Brayards Road had a dog, whose friendship towards me only consisted of not taking a piece of the flesh of my leg for a meal. He had on a previous occasion mistaken me for the vet and I had never bothered to disillusion him: he was terrified of the vet. I always hated a visit to the Blackmores, I was not afraid of the dog, but a visit to this family always seemed to give me problems. It was as though there was a *jinx* on the place! Dogs identify humans by their odour and I must be fair to the animal the Blackmore dog by 1965 had accustomed itself to my aftershave. It now took no notice of me whenever I visited the shop on Fridays to buy sweets and chocolates for my children. My presence was no longer regarded as a threat. I tended to patronize the shop, the Blackmores were good for my practice.They recommended me to their customers whenever there was any mention by their customers of their need for a new doctor.

It was in the sixties when I purchased my first Austin Mini from Eric Beaver the manager of the garage in Barry Road. This car was one of the first models and like all new cars it had teething troubles. Eric Beaver however always dropped everything whenever I was in trouble for he was the nephew of 'Old Beaver', the porter at King's College in the Strand, whom I remembered, and who remembered me, from my student days there in 1943. There were so few students at King's at that period in the war, he probably remembered everyone by first name too.

In 1966, there was an occasion when Eric Beaver could not be of any assistance to me. I have however to be fair to the man who has now departed this world, his foresight had an interest in the final outcome of the incident. He told me when I bought the mini prevention was better than cure and his advice that I have a secret switch on the ignition circuit in the car, to prevent it being started without permission, paid off.

I had responded to a call for a visit to the Blackmores one Thursday afternoon in May 1966, and for a change the weather was glorious: a fierce sun beat out of a cloudless sky. I parked my car outside the Blackmore house, locked it, and went inside. I have already mentioned it was Thursday, it was the day when I took my half-day and although I was on call for visits I had no evening surgery to rush back to. I therefore had time to accept the patient's hospitality after I had completed my examination to remain for a cup of tea and a chat. I must have been in the house for nearly an hour before I packed my bag to leave. I went outside into the bright sunshine but could not believe my eyes, where my car had been parked there was now just empty space.

I was certain that I had taken all the precautions of immobilising my vehicle before leaving it and thought someone must have found the location of my secret switch and driven the mini away. It must be remembered that car theft in the sixties was not so prevalent as it is today. Very few people had cars, few people therefore knew how to drive one.

The weather being glorious and not wanting to disturb the Blackmores, I decided to walk to the police station in Queens Road and report my loss. I had however only gone a few yards, to the corner of Brayards Road and Caulfield Road when, to my amazement, I saw my little car being pushed down the incline of Caulfield Road by two teenage boys. They had managed to open my car door, I even found when I had retrieved the vehicle they had a key in the ignition. They had however not been able to find the location of the hidden switch and had not been able to start the vehicle. The boys had obviously then decided to push the car into an area away from the site of its capture, to a place where they could give it closer inspection without fear of being apprehended.

As soon as I spotted my car I chased down the road after it, at the same time shouting, *'Stop thieves! Stop thieves!'* My young rascals however had a head start on me, although they could hear me, they decided to push harder. The car was almost at the bottom of the road, where it ends in Lugard Road, when an amazing thing happened.

The event could not have come at a more opportune moment for I was almost exhausted as I was carrying too much weight at the time and I was carrying a heavy medical bag. I lost my footing. I was still about eight feet from the car when my feet must have reached an oil patch on the road and I went slithering along it, completely out of control. I was luckily within striking distance of my persecutors, my mind however at that moment was more concentrated as to how to prevent myself from sustaining a serious injury than recovering my car. The momentum of my slip had carried my body after a couple of yards into the position of being 45 degrees from the horizontal, and the weight of my medical case which was still being firmly held in my right hand was pulling me to the ground. With my case almost trailing on the ground, my feet collided into the legs of one of the car pushers. I was travelling at speed – albeit not of my own volition – but my involuntary attack on one of the thieves had an effect which certainly could not have been better planned!

The stricken boy, after he had been forced by my attack on his legs to collide into the back of my car went sprawling into the road. The other pusher – who was using the front bonnet for leverage – feeling the car suddenly jerk, stopped pushing, and looked for the cause of the sudden increase in momentum. He turned around, and when he saw his friend lying in the road and me almost on top of him decided that cowardice was the best policy. He ran off down the road away from the incident.

He was soon joined in the chase away from the car by the boy whom I had sent sprawling and who had rapidly regained the vertical position. To my surprise, they were now joined by a boy whom I had not previously seen. He had been in the driving seat steering the pushed car: this boy looked as though he must have been all of ten years old. He jumped out of the now stationary vehicle and chased after his colleagues who had left him to *face the music*.

I was however in no position to give chase after the boys. Besides being exhausted after the pursuit down the road I was battered and bruised from my entanglement with the legs of one of the boys. My problems had not ended with the collision, for after he had been sent sprawling I had struck the bumper of the car with my knee. On reflection, the impact on the soft boy had prevented me from having a far more serious injury. Had I not struck the fellow I would have struck a solidly-built car at speed. I suppose I have to thank him for being in the line of collision. At the time, I would have clouted him for causing me so much physical and emotional distress. As he was not at hand, I sat down in the driver's seat of the car nursing a bruised knee, with a feeling of relief at having rescued the vehicle.

This car gave me more problems than I had imagined. Although it had a front-wheel drive which enabled me to negotiate the snowy roads of the winter much better than any car which I had previously owned, the wheels being smaller than average and the snow being higher, I had several punctures a day. I believed that as I was driving in snow on pack ice tiny icicles were penetrating my tyres and giving me punctures. It could have been that ice was forming on the air inlets and allowing the air from the inner tubes to escape. In any event, of necessity, I had to negotiate side roads to do my visits and these roads are always the last ones to receive attention from the local authority when it comes to snow clearing. Tubeless tyres had not yet made their appearance, and I spent one unhappy period in the winter of constantly changing wheels. It reached the stage when I actually bought two extra spare wheels to make my work easier.

One day, I thanked God for having given me the foresight to behave in this fashion. On leaving a house after doing a visit to a child suffering from tonsillitis in St James Road, Bermondsey, I had the unnerving experience of seeing three of my tyres flat. I spent the next hour changing the wheels. At least I had three spares!

There came the time in the early sixties when I had so many patients on my list – too many for a single-handed doctor – I just had to have assistance. I therefore advertised for an assistant with a view to partnership and a young fellow applied who appeared to me to be ideally suited for the job. Just one problem – no car. I therefore bought a second car for his use. He had the use of it for exactly three weeks, the car then became useless. Not exactly useless, superfluous! He left me! He had the decency however not to take the car with him, after all it was a new one! At the time of his leaving I thought he had been using my job as a staging post before he emigrated to America and I was not too happy at his behaviour. He had told me nothing of considering a post abroad when he had accepted the assistantship. I found out much later however that I had been wrong in my supposition. He sent me a letter of apology from some small town in New Jersey, giving me his reasons for leaving me. He had not liked working in the Peckham area, and as he also had second thoughts about working in the National Health Service had decided to take his talents abroad.

It was many years afterwards when I learned the true reason for his hasty departure from my practice. He had as a student sown his *wild oats* with a nurse who had provided him with a son and heir and he had, although willing to provide for the son, not been willing to marry the mother. Now, when he came to work for me in Peckham, to his obvious distress, he found the pair to be patients of mine. He was going to find his *oats* thrown under his nose constantly had he accepted a partnership with me. He had fled! I suppose I would have done the same in his situation.

Les Kwasny then became my assistant in 1963, but as he possessed his own car, my brand-new car was put into my garage. I became a two-car family with only one driver. It was only some years afterwards when to my astonishment my wife, Louise, took it upon herself to learn how to drive and make use of the second car.

For tax purposes, my accountant advised me to change my car every two years and as my supplier Eric Beaver had now changed his franchise to the

Hillman group, I became the owner of a new *Hillman Imp*. The *imp*, I still see one occasionally on the road is I believe one of the prettiest-looking cars I have ever set my eyes upon. It was a beautiful-looking car, but like all things too beautiful, the problems which followed were mountainous. For some reason my little *imp* had an uncontrollable liking for Colyton Road, which lies off Forest Hill Road, and faces Peckham Rye Park.

The *imp*, whenever it was in this area would decide to stop, the engine would cut out. I spent hours in garages trying to find out the cause, with no success. It reached the stage that I became paranoid when I had a visit in the Colyton, Mundania, Therapia, or Marmora Road areas, on Fridays. It was as though there was a ghost in the area who switched off the engine and would not allow it to restart. The engine with this gremlin in the boot – its engine was at the rear – would just give up. No amount of attention on my part was able to repair the supernatural fault. It appeared as if the car had decided to spend the weekend in a congenial spot, parked opposite a park, instead of being confined in a brick garage. *Remember the Sabbath day to keep it holy,* one of the ten commandments, was going to be respected by my *imp*, whether I liked it or not.

The number of times the car was parked outside one house in Marmora Road led to some suspicion on the part of the owner of the house outside which the *imp* was parked. Four weeks in succession my *imp* was stranded outside this house on Friday afternoon, and when a friend drove me down in his

220

car on Sunday, of the fourth week, to give me a tow back to my garage, the house owner came out to greet us.

He was a man in his late sixties, with a walrus moustache, bat ears, protruding dirty-brown teeth and an evil smile. This made him look like one of the fierce Gods which one sees outside an Indian temple. A sword in his hand, and the driver of the *imp* would not now be writing down this chronicle of events.

'Do you know?' he shouted, with his face only inches away from mine and with what can only be described as a look which could kill on it,

'that you are stopping me from parking MY car outside MY house every weekend? Why the hell don't you park your monstrosity further down the road?'

With a forced smile on my face I apologetically explained to him that my car did not deliberately park itself outside his house on Friday afternoons. It had always stalled in the middle of the road. I had been forced to push it into the side of the road outside his house to prevent an obstruction. I realised immediately after I had my statement the enormity of my mistake and how stupid I had been. I should never have mentioned his house at all! I tried to placate him by offering him one of my cigarettes and this he ungraciously took. It made no difference. He was not appeased.

'If I find your car parked outside my house any weekend in the future,' he said with a leer,

'you are going to find your car jacked-up with no wheels.'

I was careful not to park my car anywhere near his house afterwards and when my *imp* stalled four weeks later near his house, I purposely pushed it around the corner, away from the eyes of the persecuted householder. When on that Friday I had pushed the car into its new parking site, outside a house a good twenty yards from its previous site, my aim had been to keep it as far as possible from its previous refuge. I had not bothered to pay any attention to the surroundings, or the notice which stood at the entrance of this house.

On Sunday morning, when my friend took me to tow my car away, whom should we see come out of his house as we drove past but my persecutor, the fellow who had threatened to remove my wheels should he find the car outside his house. He had two, large, shaggy-looking dogs with him, and having spotted us, had no intention of allowing us to leave without making his presence felt.

He came over to us as we were preparing to put a rope between the cars. The dogs obviously gave him a feeling of power for he gave me a *dig* in the ribs. This *dig* was not severe or serious enough to warrant being called an assault, it was just to point out that he was there – that I should pay attention! He then bellowed in my ear,

'I hope you have seen the notice!'

I must admit I had not. I had been too busy attending to my car and had not looked at it until he mentioned it.

'*It reads for sale!* Buy the bloody thing! It's got a garage! It will save you parking outside my house!'

He walked off before I could reply.

222

The *imp* had been such a good car that when I came to sell it the speedometer reading was only 11,000 miles. I told the car dealer when I came to give it in part-exchange the 'clock' had never been tampered with. I was honest. It had not. As a busy general practitioner he was questioning the low mileage. As I had naturally lied that the car had given me good service, he wondered why in two-and-half years I had only done such a low mileage. What I had failed to tell him was, it was only the engine of the car which had done 11,000 miles. The wheels had probably done 17,000 miles – 6,000 miles by pushing!

I have never been a particular car lover and in the early years always left my car unlocked whenever I visited a patient's home. One day, after visiting a patient in Oglander Road, I found my car occupied by four young urchins, who were rummaging through it like woodlice. My first shouted exclamation even before I had reached the vehicle was,

'What the hell are you doing in my car?'

One boy, clutching one of my precious cigarette lighters which I had inadvertently left behind, fled. The others however got out slowly and holding various bits of worthless items, stood sullenly at the side of the car.

'You try getting into my car again and I'll give you a good hiding,' I said, as I let myself into the driving seat.

'Touch one of us and I'll get the police on to you!' said the eldest lad. This young rascal must have been at the most ten years old!

There was no point in my pursuing a losing battle. I had been well and truly chastised by a boy who obviously did not know who I was. I was certainly not his doctor! This young lad however taught me a salutary lesson. I never ever left my car unlocked again!

* * *

Homosexuality was a criminal offence when I first commenced in practice. I knew almost nothing about it except that it was supposed to be rife in public schools, the navy and prisons: in places where boys and men were herded together for long periods without feminine contact. I had no experience of it and did not know anyone who was one. Homosexuals, lesbians and men who dressed up in women's clothes – transvestites – were just funny people about whom I had read about, they were just names to me. The forty years in general practice has certainly opened my eyes and my mind to the real world in which we live.

A house in Grove Lane – I will not mention the number for fear of embarrassing the present occupants whom I do not know and are not pertinent to this story – which I used to visit regularly from 1954 - 1970 to an old lady crippled with arthritis was populated – except for the old lady – by men. She was the only female in the house and she was George's mother.

George, a tall, dark, handsome fellow, who worked in the docks, was at the time the last person in the world I would have believed to be homosexual. What however should have given me a clue was that he wore one of his mother's wedding rings on a gold chain as a necklace. But as I have already remarked, I suffered from a disease called inexperience.

This house in Grove Lane was owned by John Howe, an intellectual man in his late forties, fond of classical music and literature, who had a stream of friends live with him. He lived in the upstairs flat of this large house which stands in its own grounds. These friends, all men, – he appeared to ring the changes quite frequently – shared his luxurious flat with him. What used to surprise me, these men were of the rough type, completely his opposites intellectually: men, whom I would have expected he would not have wished to be associated with; whose company he would have avoided like the plague. In my stupidity, I believed that he was some sort of dogooder, a peculiar type of fellow who went overboard with his charity to the poor and neglected.

The war was still fresh in one's memory, people were still kind to one another and I knew that John Scott had served as an officer in the army. He was therefore in my opinion behaving as an officer and gentleman should, he was providing for homeless down-and-outs. When I reminisce, my *naivety* must have had no equal. These poor and neglected men worked as dock labourers with union cards. They all almost certainly earned more than I did! What also used to puzzle me, these friends of John, all in their late teens and early twenties, were constantly in my surgery for advice and treatment. I saw more cases of haemorrhoids (piles) in one week from his flat sharers than I had in my whole army service. The strange thing was, the age groups were identical! One of his friends even had a rectal prolapse which I was unable to reduce and I had to get the fellow hospitalised. I was too busy at the time working single-handedly trying to build up a practice to sit down and rationalise why John's friends had so much *bum trouble!*

John's own bedroom, I visited him in 1957 when he had a severe attack of influenza, had an air of femininity about it. The curtains were frilly and flowery and the sideboard and wardrobe bedecked with trinkets. The room reeked of perfume. John however was the managing director of a perfume company and I thought it only natural that he would find use for his own products. In my mind therefore, the flower-decked room and the heady-fragrance which flowed from it to the rest of the house could be explained by the profession of the owner of the house. My wife incidentally always looked forward to one of my visits to John's flat, he invariably gave me a box of perfumed soaps to bring home as a gift for her. I believe my wife made me visit his home unnecessarily at times instead of making the occupants come to the surgery: she knew that she would be rewarded for her kindness. Our home reeked like a *harlot's handbag* for weeks afterwards!

It was only in 1971, many years after John had moved out of the area and rented out the house that George, who still lived in the downstairs flat, succeeded in opening my eyes as to the cause of John's friends *bum trouble.*

John had rented the upstairs flat to a South African couple and after they had been in the flat for about ten months George came to see me one day in a state of acute anxiety. He was so overwrought, it was some time before he became calm enough to admit to me that he, and all the previous occupants of the house were, and had been, homosexual.

The reason for George's confession was a strange one. The South African couple upstairs had become patients of mine soon after their arrival in the flat as the wife had been eight months pregnant. Indeed, six weeks after they registered with me I had the privilege of delivering their second baby. The husband was a dentist who had come to this country to take a specialist course in Guy's Hospital, but after remaining in London for nine months had decided to accept another training post in Liverpool. For some reason his wife did not immediately accompany him, perhaps there was no suitable accommodation at the time for a couple blessed with two young children.

The dentist's wife, after having spent a month on her own in the upstairs flat decided late one evening that George – the handsomest fellow she had ever set eyes upon – with whom she had on several occasions had a friendly conversation was someone in her husband's absence she would like to share her bed. She had lured him upstairs on the previous night on the pretext of requiring him to repair her electric iron. She had told George she had been ironing her sheets when her iron had suddenly failed and she desperately needed his help. What she had failed to tell him was that she wanted George himself to press her sheets with his own body whilst she was lying on them. George knew immediately on his arrival in the flat what she had meant for she had prepared herself for this 'ironing' in her most seductive garb. George admitted to me that he had never in his whole life ever fancied a woman. He had therefore not known and not been able to cope with this situation.

He had burst into tears and fled! He had not slept a wink that night and for this reason had come to see me as an emergency. There was no doubt in my mind that his 'fondness' for the opposite sex had produced an acute anxiety state! It was only then, in the course of the consultation, that the owner of the house was mentioned. He was discussed at length, and his relationship with the other occupants of the house was then brought to light.

8

Sad Tales

Mr Ernest Saunders was an *old codger* when it was my good fortune to take him under my wing in 1980, he was in his late eighties at the time. He had been a patient of the Cook-Healy partnership, prior to this the MacDonald-Wilson partnership: it could be said therefore that I had inherited him!

He first came to see me in the winter of 1980, and walked, rather shuffled into the surgery with the greatest difficulty. On examination, I found that he had gross oedema of both feet and the swelling was so extensive it had spread up his legs as far as his knees. How he got about puzzled me. I wondered why he had not sent for me to visit him when he was in such distress. I had visited people on hundreds of occasions with symptoms of far less importance but I held my tongue; one did not question such a forthright man as Ernest. His first statement as he sat down in the chair in my consulting room clearly pointed out to me that in spite of his age he was determined to become my friend.

'You know that girl in reception, the young one, the girl with the beautiful face, I think her name is Bernie, well, I can't see her legs as she is wearing a long skirt. You can tell her from me I wouldn't mind a night in bed with her.'

His eyes were pointedly focused on mine as he related the narrative. 'You can have the one in the nurse's uniform, the old one!'

I marvelled at his sex drive, but as I had never treated this man before thought it wise not to make a retort. I did not know what the reaction would be from a man of such tender years. I examined him, prescribed the necessary treatment, and asked him to come back and see me in a week. I should have known better. I had asked him to make an appointment and he had done so, but only because he had at the time wanted to get away quickly and avoid an argument. Not for one moment had he any intention of keeping it. Why a doctor who had been in practice for over thirty years should have expected an old boy with Ernest's temperament to keep his appointment I now find hard to understand. I should have guessed at what kind of a patient I had inherited from his opening remarks, but to be fair to me, I had never met a man like Ernest Saunders before.

Of one thing I was certain, our Ernest was in congestive heart failure so after surgery on the day he had been due to see me I went round to see him at his house. I rang the bell, knocked and knocked. There was no response. I went again on the following day – still no response. On the third day, when I once again got no reply at his house, I came back to the surgery and asked one of the receptionists to telephone the police. I told her to inform them that Ernest could possibly have departed this life and as he lived alone no one would have been aware. The face of the receptionist to whom I addressed my request creased with laughter. She had just seen Ernest dragging his body, with a basketful of shopping behind him, in Rye Lane!

Six weeks after our first encounter, after I had finished morning consultations and gone out on my visits and been forced to return to the surgery to collect a new prescription pad, I saw Ernest sitting in the waiting room. I asked the receptionist what he was doing sitting there, her answer was precise and needed no interpretation.

'*He has come to see you.* I told him you had finished surgery and were booked up for tonight but he wouldn't listen. He just said, don't worry yourself, he will see me when he comes back.'

He was right! I saw him immediately. One does not keep a man who is nearly ninety and takes the trouble to come to the surgery – waiting.

Ernest appeared to have no close family. The only person related to him was a niece who lived some distance away and to her credit she came to see him regularly and provided him with whisky and cigarettes. He had evidently always had to fend for himself and as often as I tried to draw from him some details of his life before I came on the scene I was unsuccessful. The only details I ever discovered were, he had been born in Peckham at the turn of the century and had served in the trenches in the 1914-18 war.

'*The army*' – he once remarked when I tried to extract information from him by relating my own

231

experiences in the Forces – *'is a "god-awful" place. All muck and bullets. I should know!'*

With regard to marriage he just laughed whenever I spoke about it. However hard I tried, I never found out whether he had ever been married or whether he had any children. No one except the niece ever put in an appearance while I attended the old chap. I thought, as he was so reticent about speaking of his past life it was possible – he was after all eighty-nine – his nearest and dearest could have departed this life, just by virtue of their ages.

Ernest lived in Muschamp Road, on the third floor of a three-storey semidetached house, the bottom two floors of which were empty, dilapidated and dirty. Ernest told me that he had lived in the house on this top floor for over fifty years! Now no one, but no one, was going to get him out of it; except in a box. He did not own the house, he just rented the top floor. When he had an attack of pneumonia in 1987, and in view of his age I tried to persuade him to go into hospital for treatment, he adamantly refused.

'I know what will happen, *they* will move my stuff out as soon as I have left the house,' he said.

The *they*, I was assured by Ernest, were the owners of the house. I treated him at home and as he was a tough old blighter, he responded to antibiotic therapy with the same result as if he had been a youngster. As the man was in the house on his own and it would have been remiss of me to leave him to fend for himself I was forced to seek the help of the social services. He was such a fighter, he would only suffer their help so long as he was confined to his bed: the moment he became ambulant he gave them marching orders. The social services then offered Ernest alternative accommodation, but he would have none of it. It was useless for me to point out the social services were only acting out of kindness. He was a controlled tenant, he would remain where he was, until the Good Lord called him.

When I had first managed to gain admittance to Ernest's house I had asked him why the two lower floors were unoccupied, and he explained that the previous owner had sold the house to an Indian fellow who lived in Wolverhampton. The Indian, Ernest told me, really wanted the whole house for his own use as he had a large family, but there was no way he was going to get it. The fellow who had bought the property had obviously not reckoned on the *bloody-mindedness* of Ernest. Ernest was determined to prevent the owner from occupying the premises at all costs, even the bottom two floors. He had even refused entrance to builders who came to do repairs. The owner, to his credit, never harassed Ernest, nor did he make any effort to get Ernest evicted. He naturally thought that Father Time would do the work for him. The landlord was anathema to Ernest, he could never say a good word about the fellow. He had made up his mind – in spite of his age he was in complete command of his faculties – the landlord was determined to clear him out of the premises one way or another. Whatever I said to the contrary had not the slightest effect.

In all my visits to Ernest I only encountered his landlord once, and this was on a bright day in

March 1987. There were three-flights of steep stairs to get to Ernest's lodgings and when on that day I knocked the landlord opened the door to let me in. He had seen me park my car with the BMA badge on the windscreen outside the house and had opened the front door to save the old boy having to trek down three flights of stairs. He was quite amiable, asked me about Ernest's health, and whether he could be of any assistance in making his lot more comfortable. Ernest's reply when I told him what the landlord had done and said was,

'*the landlord's a bastard!* They told me there is some dry rot in the house and I let his builders in. The bastard knows I've got a bad chest, he is having the two floors downstairs painted with special foul-smelling paint. When the builders are finished he is going to close the windows and fix them so they can't be opened. You see, the bastard will make sure I die in agony!'

Ernest spent most of his life in his front-sitting room, but as he became older and weaker, he transferred his living quarters to the back of the house where he had a bed. This room was an attic with a sloping roof, it was tiny and uncomfortable: at the back of the room was a sink with a gas water heater. He appeared to be quite happy in this room and the small table in the middle of the room was always overflowing with cans of beer, half-bottles of whisky and cigarettes. The only other articles of furniture in this room were two kitchen chairs which had seen better days – the leather seats had worn through to the wooden bases – an old electric fire, and an Ercol armchair of which he was very proud.

I had long given up telling Ernest that the number of cigarettes he was smoking was having a bad effect on his chest. He smoked about twenty-five cigarettes a day and had a perpetual cough. Finally the stage was reached when Ernest could no longer cope on his own and he had to be provided with daily nursing care. Now we had a problem! Ernest told me that he was not prepared to allow more than one nurse to attend him. No more than one person would be allowed to have a set of keys. He did not want *'dozens of nurses having dozens of sets of keys and be robbed wholesale.'* As it was impossible to promise him that he would always have the same one and only nurse there appeared to be no way out of the dilemma except to allow the fellow to die a long lingering death on his own without help of any kind. I was faced with an impossible situation. I begged the social services to help me and they came to the rescue by offering him a flat on the ground floor of a warden-controlled home. When I told Ernest I could no longer come to see him just to watch him die in agony without help he agreed to take up the offer and move.

'I suppose that bastard of a landlord has put you up to this' were the actual words of thanks I got as a reward for my efforts. Ernest was moved from the house in which he had lived for over fifty years, in safety, one Wednesday. On Friday he was in hospital. He had lasted just two days in his new environment before being caught up in our modern violent society.

The residents of this sheltered accommodation who live on the ground floor are warned not to open the windows or doors leading to the outside garden area, to prevent intruders entering the building. Unfortunately, it is not possible to put bars on all windows or doors as all the occupants are elderly and in the event of fire in the main building their escape would be cut off. Ernest was not going to take orders from anyone.

He was in the home for just two days when an intruder let himself into his flat through the open kitchen window, held a knife to his throat and kicked him in the chest breaking four of his ribs. The burglar then ransacked the room, stole his watch and a few other valuables. The stolen articles however were priceless, they were a memory of his past life.

I saw Ernest on Sunday after he was allowed back to his flat from hospital, he really should have been kept in, the hospital however needed his bed. I knew just by looking at him that Ernest's remaining time in this world was going to be short. All the fight had gone out of him. He had been persuaded by me, his niece, and the social services, that he was no longer safe in his home in Muschamp Road and that we were going to place him in a safe environment. We had failed him!

Five days after his attack he developed pneumonia. As there were no facilities to nurse him in the home I was reluctantly forced to arrange hospital admission. I waited for the ambulance to arrive and before the attendants put him on the stretcher he insisted on shaking hands with me. His words brought tears to my eyes.

'You've been a good mate of mine these last few

years doc, thanks for all you've done. You really are a good bloke. *We won't see each other again.*'

He kept his word. He died the next day.

* * *

The Plymouth Brethren, called by that name as the sect began its life in the city of Plymouth, is a community of Christians founded in 1830. This sect, although very small, has entered my life on two occasions.

The first occasion was in my student days when a fellow student, a member of the sect, tried to convert me to his beliefs. When he found that he had failed to do so, he made me his best friend. He it was who explained to me the different divisions of the brethren, the Exclusives, the Neutrals and the true Plymouth Brethren. He spent hours trying to explain the differences of these divisions: not being conversant with Christian doctrine I could not understand a word he was talking about. I however found it strange and embarrassing that the rest of the students, all Christians, treated him as a big joke.

One particular day, he came into lunch in the refectory when we were already seated, went down on his knees at the table at which I was sitting and began to preach a sermon about idol worship and the sins of the flesh. The students stood up as a body – the performance must have been rehearsed – and danced around him chanting '*Wimjam! Wimjam! Wimjam!*' drowning his sermon. He preached louder. They shouted louder. Neutral in this clash of faiths, I grabbed hold of the kneeling preacher and frogmarched him out of the refectory. Outside, out of the earshot of the 'blasphemers', I gave him a severe lecture on when and where to preach his beliefs. He had no right to allow religion be subjected to ridicule.

The second time this sect entered my life was in November 1953, when I was in my own practice in Bellenden Road, and a visit to a Mrs Gregson was requested. Mrs Gregson I learned was a seventy-seven-year-old lady who lived in Arbuthnot Road, New Cross. I had only been in practice in the area for ten months and did not know the family, but I had no difficulty at all after examining the patient in diagnosing the old lady as having bronchopneumonia.

Mrs Gregson, a widow, lived in this large Victorian house with her married daughter, the daughter's husband and three young grandchildren. The old lady was so ill I suggested to her that I should get her admitted to hospital but she adamantly refused. Now I had real problems! Although I honestly believed I could cure the old lady even if she remained at home, not one member of the family volunteered to nurse her or even to provide her with food. I was told that she had at one time been a member of the Plymouth Brethren, but for reasons never given to me, had left. Her family had then been instructed by the Brethren clergy never to speak to her again.

She lived upstairs in the large house, the rest of the family lived downstairs, but never, except for her son-in-law, communicated in any way. They never even wished her the time of day if they met. The house however being very large, avoiding each other proved easy. Her family, as true believers, were even forbidden to *break bread* with her. Evidently, the clergymen in charge of their sect had made every effort to get her to return and having failed to do so had passed the edict that she be excommunicated. In their opinion, she was not even a person fit to be spoken to. On being told on my first visit the way this family conducted itself to its own kith and kin, I realised my problem was going to be a serious one. I was a young man, with little experience in general practice, nevertheless, the previous close encounter with this sect now stood me in good stead.

Mrs Gregson had been lying in bed with a high temperature and a racking nonproductive cough and not one member of the family, all congregated downstairs in the living room, had taken the trouble to accompany me. I therefore had no choice but to go downstairs after examining my patient and explain to the family the seriousness of the old lady's illness. The son-in-law, not a member of the sect, made every effort to persuade his wife that in the cause of common humanity she should undertake to nurse her mother. His efforts were unsuccessful. His mother had sinned. If the Good Lord decided to take her mother away she was not going to lift a finger to stop him! It was now my turn at the persuasion stakes.

I gave the daughter a scripture lesson. I pointed out that honouring one's parent is a distinct commandment, one of the ten commandments, the only one which gives a reward for its fulfilment. By nursing her mother, she would at little cost to herself be buying herself an extra term of life insurance. As this was guaranteed by God himself, she could not choose a better guarantor. The prohibition of *breaking bread* with her mother could be fulfilled to the letter by not providing her mother with any bread. If she did not give her mother any bread, she would not be breaking her clergyman's edict. To my astonishment, her mother never received any bread while she was being nursed!

The cumulative persuasive efforts of myself and the son-in-law bore fruit. We managed to persuade the daughter to nurse her mother during her illness, even though we were unable to get her to agree to make permanent peace. I had no complaint, she carried out her commitment and nursed her mother. Her mother however was constantly reminded of her lack of faith and made to feel the animosity of being a traitor to her religion. I never ever found out why her mother had left the true faith except to postulate that her son-in-law might have had something to do with it. He left his wife two years after his mother-in-law's illness, and the reason for leaving – he told me so himself – was his wife's beliefs. He could not take the religious fervour which permeated his house and made his everyday existence purgatory. He has never returned.

The old lady recovered completely. As the years went by, perhaps because the daughter had lost her husband, the daughter and the grandsons became a little more tolerant. They even condescended to say 'good morning' and 'good evening' to their granny if she happened to pass them on the stairs. Their behaviour towards their grandmother had previously been abominable. She had never forgotten their birthdays, had always bought them presents for Christmas, but no thanks had ever been received. If the grandmother had previously met them on the stairs she had always greeted them: they had ignored her. What torment she must have suffered to have lived in the same house as her grandsons whom she loved and be totally ignored by them! She had been treated worse than a stranger: a stranger would at least have had the satisfaction of being acknowledged.

The boys', strict, one-parent, religious upbringing, has definitely had an effect on them even though there has been some relaxation in their relationship to the outside world. They have all remained members of the Plymouth Brethren, attended all their meetings whether religious or social and kept all the commandments without question or rebellion. To be completely honest, two of the boys it must be said have strayed a little. I am certain their choice of friends would not at all meet with the approval of the 'higher hierarchy'.

Ten years ago, the youngest boy, Michael, now a man in his forties, reverted to strict religious beliefs. Even worse, he became a fanatic. He became so religious he even cut himself off from his mother and would not see his brothers in case he became contaminated by their contact with their chosen friends. His family were now not religious enough for him! He locked himself up in his back-upstairs room in his mother's house so as not to breathe the same polluted air and become plague-ridden.

It was all very sad. I had always taken a keen interest in the boys' education for in spite of their religious fervour they had all been very bright. They had attended local elementary schools and at the age of eleven had gained scholarships to Alleyns' Grammar School. They had all gone to university and obtained good degrees. It could not be said that they were a dumb lot, incapable of original thought.

Michael, in spite of his religious fanaticism, still however related to me in a friendly fashion. He had known me since he was four years old and when his mother in desperation turned to me for help, he agreed to see me. I was shown up to his room by his mother, then found myself in an abnormal situation. He was in no way belligerent, but insisted that he lock the door behind us with a key – to keep out the spirits of the polluted air which contaminated the house. It did not take a doctor to determine that this fellow was definitely mentally disturbed! The house had the most obnoxious smell of cats' mess which I have ever encountered. Closing the door without locking it would have been quite sufficient!

We had a long chat about his work, the environment and the general world situation: his fanaticism had strangely not affected his work pattern. I suggested to him that he should take some time off work to review things and he agreed. When I told him that the only person able to give a certificate for absence from work in the circumstances about which we had spoken was a psychiatrist he agreed to see one. I was overjoyed and made the necessary appointment for him to see one the very next day. To my absolute astonishment he kept the appointment.

Unfortunately, when I went back to see him to ask what the psychiatrist had recommended, he told me in no uncertain terms what he thought of this specialist. The psychiatrist was a blaspheming-heathen, a pagan, a devil's disciple. In no way would he now be prepared to accept treatment except from me, or from a practising Plymouth Brother. To find a psychiatrist who practised his faith I knew would be almost impossible, the problem however never arose. Two days after my last visit to him I received an urgent call from his mother to come at once, her son was bleeding to death!

Michael had suddenly become aware, as if by magic, that he was a normal man and had normal feelings. He developed a fancy for a member of the opposite sex! He has never at any time disclosed to me who the lady was, but his sexual desire at the time had become overwhelming, more than he could bear. He decided after having given the matter much thought that there was only one cure. He told me that he had wrestled with the *devil* – his sexual desire – for three days, but had been unable to conquer it. He had then cut off the *devil* – the end of his penis – which in his distorted mind was the cause of all his frustration and lust.

Luckily for him, the pain and loss of blood seemed to produce some momentary sanity. He shouted to his mother for help and she sent for me. I sent him into hospital as an emergency and stressed to the doctor who agreed to admit him this cut had not been an accidental one. He had also not undergone a ritual circumcision. The doctor did not have to expect to be invited to a party. In the Jewish faith there is always a party after a circumcision, with this patient there was not going to be one! He not only required a quick suture to save his organ he required some brain treatment too.

Fortunately, it was possible to stitch his *devil* back, and he was given psychiatric treatment whilst still a hospital inpatient. Although I have seen him on numerous occasions since this episode in his life, we do not mention this period.

This story has a happy ending. Michael has now remained stable for some years and has married. Whether this partner was the cause of his sexual fantasies which led to the *cut*, I do not know. What I do know is, he is happily married and the couple have two children.

* * *

Cyprus, a crown colony since 1925, went through a period of turmoil in 1931, when serious disturbances broke out as the Greek population wanted Enosis (union with Greece). Turmoil persisted until 1955 when, as the Greek, Turkish and British Governments could not find a solution to the problem an atmosphere of increased irritability was brought about. After much further strife and negotiation, Cyprus was allowed to become an independent state by an act of Parliament, in 1960. If anyone thought this would bring an end to the years of conflict between the Turkish and Greek communities on the island, they were mistaken. Cyprus is still not at peace with itself. In the unstable times of the fifties and sixties many Cypriots left the island to live in this country, and many were from the intellectual and artistic community.

Mr Demetrious, who became a patient of mine in 1968, had been a university lecturer, and came to live in Underhill Road, East Dulwich. He was a Greek, in his sixties, had retired from his faculty early, but having been paid by the British and friendly with the authorities had not been made to feel too welcome in the new Cyprus. He had a heart condition from which he had suffered for years and this malady was not helped by the stress of having to leave his birthplace and roots. I now became the *fall guy* who had to treat his physical problems for his political beliefs! Having a bad heart necessitated my calling at his home on numerous occasions, the one problem however I did not have to worry about was his nursing care. In this field he was well cared for, his daughter and her grown-up children also lived in the area. They loved the old man, came to visit him several times a day, and he could not have had better treatment if they had lived with him. His daughter rather strangely had married a Turk in Cyprus, but how this had come about I found it politically unwise to ask and never found out.

One morning, in the late seventies, Mr Demetrious sent for a home visit before morning surgery and I did the visit on the way to the surgery from my home in Brockley. He complained of having had a bad night, had coughed up a little blood and was feeling weak and tired. On examination I found that his congestive heart failure had worsened just that little bit from my previous visit so I altered his medication to combat any further deterioration. He had some fluid in his lung bases and a little ankle swelling, but the same findings had been present for two years. I did not feel at the time his condition in any way warranted hospitalisation and indeed, he expressed the wish that he did not want to go into hospital. He had answered the door to me himself, he was mobile, and I was therefore quite happy to leave him. I told him to continue on the new regime for a week when I would call and review his treatment.

He would as a general rule detain me with a political discussion, this particular morning had proved no exception. He had discussed the relationship of Cyprus and Israel with me many times as he knew that my mother lived in Jerusalem and he told me that he had himself when living in Cyprus been to Israel eight times to celebrate Christmas in the Holy city. He was a joy to talk to: he was a mine of information on the political figures in the Middle East as he had met them all. He could have been called an expert on the political situation in the region. I left him on that morning without any presentiment that an early call was going to be made on him by the Angel of Death.

An intriguing thing about this chap was, he had huge nude photographs of little boys, in large frames, hanging on the walls in his living room. I had never thought it worthwhile asking the identities of these children. I knew that he had grandchildren living all over the world and had not felt it decent to ask why they had all been taken whilst unclothed. The fact the children were all in the seven to ten age group I thought part of Middle East culture.

At the end of a tiring day, at the end of my evening surgery, I felt justified in being somewhat irritated when his daughter telephoned to speak to me as an emergency only a few hours after I had visited her father. She refused to leave a message with a receptionist. She had to speak to me. When I took the telephone her message was loud and clear: would I please call urgently to see her father! In case she had not been aware, I explained that I had been to see her father that morning, he had congestive heart failure and a man of his 'tender years' did not get better in five minutes. There was nothing more I could do for him! Without my knowing it, how true that last statement was. She listened to me as I continued with my protestations in silence, then said without any emotion,

'I am speaking from dad's house. I think dad is dead.'

Her blunt statement of fact momentarily staggered me. I hesitated, then said,

'Stay there. I will be with you as soon as I can.'

On arrival at the house I found her father sitting in a chair in the middle of his living room, fully dressed from the waist upwards, a dressing gown

247

around his shoulders, and a loosely-wrapped scarf round his neck. His trousers and underpants were down somewhere around his ankles. He was therefore naked from the waist down. His head was slumped forward. His eyes were closed, and his mouth – from which frothy, bloody fluid oozed – was open. There was a bucket planted in front of his chair and in the bucket was what appeared to be a few drops of urine.

It was obvious to me at first glance – even looking at him casually – I would not be having any more political arguments with poor Mr Demetrious! The remarkable thing was, he had not fallen out of the chair. He appeared to be rooted in it.

His daughter who was in the room when I arrived, was normally quite an excitable person; on this occasion however, she appeared to be calm and collected. I had told the daughter many times how seriously ill her father was, that he might have a heart attack at any time and *pop off*, and I therefore attributed her calmness to my previous warnings. I had no reason to believe there was anything unusual appertaining to this man's death and assumed that he had collapsed in the chair while going to the toilet. I had seen the chap myself a few hours earlier complaining of increasing breathlessness. Perhaps – I thought – I had underestimated the seriousness of my findings!

It is not unusual for a patient with heart trouble to be found dead on the toilet and I regarded the circumstances in which Mr Demetrious had been found to be included in this category. I had no hesitation therefore in giving the family a death certificate with the cause of death as 'congestive heart failure'. I thought this episode of finding him dead concluded my relationship with him.

I was wrong!

Mr Demetrious's granddaughter's husband came in to see me on a routine appointment about five years after the old man's death, and for many weeks afterwards gave me many a sleepless night.

This chap was a rough diamond. He was a tall, olive-skinned, handsome, Cypriot fellow, who had married this pretty granddaughter and provided her with two beautiful children. He cared for the children and his wife, but could not leave English girls alone. Two of his English girlfriends had provided him with babies. His wife who knew of his exploits and cried to me about them had become rather unfriendly to him over his behaviour. He used to confide in me too, and the only reason he gave for his sexual behaviour was that the girls chased him. Why should he refuse something handed to him on a plate, was a constant rejoinder to my admonitions. Was it his fault the girls had unwanted pregnancies? They had always told him they were on the pill! The fellow was such a plausible talker I half believed him; the other half I am sure he believed himself. He always gave me the impression he was trying to make excuses to me as he knew that I was a friend of his wife's family.

On this particular visit he came in to see me with an attack of acute bronchitis and while examining his chest he talked so much I had to tell him to shut up. He did, until I popped a thermometer under his arm to see if he had a temperature when he started talking again. His opening remarks when the thermometer finally came to its resting place caused me to stop in my tracks.

'We know who killed the old man,' he said. I stared at him in disbelief.

'I assume you are talking about your wife's grandfather,' I answered.

'Yes, the old chap who lived in Underhill Road. He was a nice old chap, he wouldn't hurt a fly. If he had not got himself involved in this nasty sex business he would still be alive today.'

His remarks staggered me.

'You mean to say, he did not have a heart attack but was murdered? Do you know what you are saying? If what you are telling me is the truth it is my duty to report the matter to the police,' I replied.

He gave me supercilious look.

'You are joking. I will deny everything I have said if you mention this conversation outside this room. The police will think you have gone funny in the head! Any person they care to question who knew the old boy will confirm that he died from natural causes. We deal with these matters in our own way.'

The old man I now learned was a bisexual, a pervert, who liked to play with little boys and little boys to play with him. He used to pay for little boys to come to him for sexual gratification and some Cypriot boys he played with regularly came on the day of his death and asked for money. On this occasion he refused. Either he had no money or perhaps they would not do what he asked to earn it. They strangled him and ransacked the house. His family knew who the culprits were, but to silence me at the time, avoid a scandal, and obtain a death certificate, had remained calm and behaved as if he had died naturally. By this time I had regained my composure.

'People who kill once and get away with it will kill again,' I said.

'No chance!' was the reply. After the old chap's death the culprits had taken fright and fled to Cyprus. They had been dealt with there.

'What happened to them?' I asked.

He ignored my question as if he had not heard it. I repeated it. I got a blank look. I repeated it again. This time he looked me straight into the eyes.

'I don't know what the devil you are talking about!' he said.

Approximately two years after he had told me his version of the grandfather's death, he fled to Cyprus himself, to escape prosecution from the police on a charge of fraud.

The whole family has now left my medical list as they have all moved out of my practice area. When I think back to the days when grandfather departed this life, I have at times been tempted to report this story which had been told to me by the grandson-in-law: I have however desisted from doing so. His statement that the boys had ransacked the old chap's room was not true! I had been in that room that morning and it was in exactly the same condition when I had returned in the evening. Not one object had been out of place. I had been in the same room on dozes of occasions, a ransacked room would obviously have been a little bit abnormal and not escaped my notice.

On reflection, I think his statement was a way to get back at his wife's family after they had turned their back on him. Why had he waited so many years to pour out this nonsensical story to me? I knew from experience that he was a person who was given to bending the truth. The police too were chasing him for his dishonesty, so much so, he had been forced to flee the country.

The only disturbing thing about the episode which at one time gave me cause for concern was when I asked Mrs Demetrious's daughter after her father's death who the naked boys were whose photographs were on her father's wall. Her answer puzzled me.

'I have no idea. They are certainly not members of our family!'

*　　*　　*

The house in which the practice is situated was *surgery-cum-home* when I first commenced to practise in Peckham, in 1953. As time passed and my family increased in size we moved, the living section of the house then became the home of housekeepers. It was necessary to fulfil one's obligations as a general practitioner under the terms of the National Health Service at the time, either for the doctor to live on the practice premises or provide a housekeeper to do so. It was really no bad thing, most of my patients did not have a telephone and would not have been able to afford one even if one was available. Telephone lines were very difficult to obtain in the fifties: there was a wait of several months after ordering a telephone before a person could actually get one.

Some of the housekeepers who occupied our premises after we left were good, some were excellent and gave value for living in *rent-free*, all expenses paid accommodation. Some however were *conniving devils*, who used the living quarters to house their relatives at my expense. Some even made use of the bathroom as public baths and probably charged the visitors for its use. None of the housekeepers however could rival our last housekeeper, darling Ella.

Ella, was in her late sixties, or early seventies, when she took up the onerous responsibility of being a housekeeper. I never found out her true age, she never told me. She had been born in the East End, was a real cockney, with all the cockney characteristics, and had lived in an area where most of the inhabitants at the time were Jews. In that environment, she evidently fitted in like a glove. She looked Jewish, and used to relate how she was always turned out of school assembly to sit with the Jewish children outside when prayers were being said. The teachers believed her to be of the Jewish faith, insisted that she join the Jewish children in their activities, and treated her occasional reluctance as a laxity of home religious observance and obstinacy. Indeed, religious observance of any kind was missing in her home. She claimed that she had never heard of Jesus until she was eight years old!

The dining room, which served my family and so many housekeepers who followed us as an eating place, a place where one could put one's feet up, was turned into a menagerie by Ella. She had three huge fish tanks, never bothered to clean the water in them and when she finally left our premises we found the original water was still in the tanks. She had not forgotten to put fish in the tanks, these poor creatures however had decided in a very short time that it was not worth living in such conditions and had passed on into the next world. Unfortunately, on their demise, they had forgotten to take their smell with them, and the smell of stinking fish added to the general stench which emanated from the dining room.

The surgery problem however was, the malodorous fumes of putrefaction which permeated through the dining-room window into the walkway outside caused Dr Healy to quicken his steps almost to a run as he passed the dining room to his consulting room in the garden from reception. He would constantly chide Lynn, the practice manager, about the smell. Dr Healy however is such a gentleman, he would never attempt to insult Ella and tell her to her face about the *running practice* he was forced into every time he passed her living quarters. When Ella was finally reprimanded about the fragrance which emanated from her dining room by Lynn, she could in all honesty state,

'the doctors don't notice anything! They would tell me if they did!'

Ella had a cat, who regarded her table as *fair game* for foraging exercises when her mistress was out of the room. I have seen the cat in the garden with a large portion of chicken in its mouth being chased by Ella, who never had a hope in hell of recovering her lost property. Ella loved cooking and baking and rather than use the kitchen, the ceiling in the dining room became the constant sufferer of her culinary experiments. When she finally left our premises we found the ceiling in this room had the same colour as the ace of spades.

The strange thing about Ella was, she herself never ever smelt. The living conditions and Ella were in complete contrast! I would often call when I was on rota duty to see whether she had taken any messages and whether there were any visits to be done – she took messages for me – and she always emerged from the dining room to come and see me in reception smelling of roses. In all the years that she was our housekeeper I never ventured into her dining room once! She never invited me in, and I felt duty-bound to respect her privacy.

Whenever I gave her a lift to one of her functions after a spell on duty, she would appear in a ball gown, immaculately-dressed, hair beautifully-fashioned, and nails polished. What I did not realise until much later, there was no possible way she could have used the bath! When her bathroom was entered when she was on holiday in Australia, water was seen seeping from the kitchen into the walkway outside and a burst water pipe was thought to be at fault. It was not a burst pipe, it was just the bath overflowing. The kitchen floor was waterlogged, and the bathroom which led from the kitchen was flooded from a bath full of stinking water. The bath could never have been used, it was full of pots and pans soaking in it; the inside of this bath had not seen the light of day for years!

The kitchen too was allowed by Ella to become a refuse pit. I can say without prejudice, now that the kitchen has been transferred into a treatment room it looks and smells very different from when Ella was in attendance. Perhaps, having a white ceiling instead of a black one, burnt-black by cooking which has not been properly supervised, has made all the difference. Perhaps, having a practice nurse who has hygiene as one of her priorities has made a difference to the smell which used to invade the atmosphere of the premises.

I have already stated that I never ventured into Ella's living quarters, this is strictly true while she remained our housekeeper. However, on the day she vacated our premises I went into the dining room to see in what condition she had left it. I simply could not believe my eyes. The place stank. I had never seen such a mess in my life. It was unbelievable. I went upstairs to drag Dr Cook down to see the state of the place as he had been instrumental in persuading me to engage Ella as our housekeeper. He looked, and without a smile said,

'I can't help it if our last housekeeper is houseproud!'

He had defused the situation in a second. I could not restrain myself from bursting into hysterical laughter and had to run from the room to contain myself.

Beetroots, can be used to make *borsht*, wine, used in salads, in pickles, in cakes, in jam making; I can even remember as a student given cooked beetroots as a sandwich filler. I have however never heard of a war being fought over this vegetable! Beetroots, are not usually a subject of concern except to a gardener who wishes to discriminate between colour, flavour or size. In our practice, in 1984, beetroots became a matter of extreme importance. A war could have been fought over the behaviour of this vegetable.

I was called by one of the receptionists one morning to see the patients toilet, someone had reported it being blocked with blood. I went. I saw. I called the plumber. He came, looked at the pool of blood in the toilet pan and gave his considered opinion.

'Some silly idiot has deposited her sanitary towel down the lavatory pan. Some people have no sense, no consideration.' He looked again, poked around a bit and was now not quite so certain.

'It could be due to someone who has had a miscarriage,' he said.

We had to agree for the water was so blood-stained. It had not flushed through the system and in our medically-trained minds there had to be a pathological reason for so much blood. All the staff were now worried as to what could be the cause of the blockage. The general feeling was, sooner or later there was going to be some police involvement: some questioning and harrassment. Apprehension was the general mood!

The blockage however could not be allowed to remain, it had to be cleared, and it was with trepidation we watched the plumber bring out his flushing rods to clear the obstruction. He had no trouble whatsoever. He just pushed his rods through the U-bend of the pan without effort – the blockage was gone! Even though we had not solved the mystery of the cause, we all breathed a sigh of relief.

We had two days of freedom, the patients were able to use the toilet to their hearts content when we were astonished to find that we had a repeat *blockage performance*. The toilet was once again blocked with what appeared to be blood. We could now however – thank heavens – remove miscarriage as one of the differential diagnoses. No girl miscarries twice in three days, unless she is having twins. Certainly not in the same toilet!

We still however had to call in the plumber. Although he was as puzzled as we were, his rods did the clearing trick in two-minutes flat. He had given such a quick and excellent performance, I am sure that after he had pulled the chain, as he stood looking at the water emptying through the now clear pan, he expected those of us who watched to clap.

A week later, when the toilet was once again blocked with what appeared to be blood in the pan, the staff now came under suspicion. In the doctors' opinions, it either had to be a member of the staff who was trying to make a point to prove that she had to give her lifeblood to work for us, or it was the work of a disgruntled patient. We thought that perhaps it was the work of a patient who did not like our receptionists and was determined to throw suspicion on them and in doing so give maximum aggravation to the doctors. Perhaps I had misdiagnosed someone and instead of taking it out on me he or she had decided to take it out on the toilet! What the most likely diagnosis however was, our sewage system had suffered a major catastrophe. The only thing which puzzled us all was the colour of the water in the pan. It was bright red. It looked like blood, had congealed bits in the liquid, and anyway in a doctor's surgery what would anyone expect to see except blood?

Once again we called in the plumber, we had no alternative. Once again he produced his rods, on this occasion however all his efforts to clear the obstruction failed. We now gave him instructions to remove the toilet pan in order to clear the blockage as we were now also determined to find the cause. The plumber told us that it was going to be a costly job to do as we asked, but what alternative did we have?

He removed the pan as requested and had no trouble whatsoever in making a diagnosis as to the cause of the blockage. To his, and it has to be said to our amazement too, he passed several large beetroots for us to inspect. These had been forced past the U-bend of the toilet pan into the waste pipe. The only person who did not show surprise at the discovery was Ella! From her reaction, we deduced she must either have been the culprit or the accomplice of the person who had perpetrated this crime. Interestingly, I was now informed Ella was at that particular time indulging in one of her culinary experiments – the making of beetroot wine. I was however in no position to prove that she was the beetroot blender. My relations with her had always been excellent, she was on friendly terms with all the doctors and she was friendly with all the staff too. We loved her in spite of all her eccentricities.

Ella however had the unfortunate habit of commencing a hobby and not completing the course. I suppose we have to be thankful for this trait in her character otherwise she might have put our sanitary system out of action for keeps! She had at one time mentioned to one of the receptionists that she would like to make beetroot wine and had discussed with her the best place for fermentation to take place. The receptionist had suggested wooden barrels. I can only assume Ella thought her beetroots would mature better in our toilet pan than in her barrels!

The lady now lives in Australia and was such a character, I hope the marsupials down under have managed to give her a wide berth. She only left us because in the end she could no longer be trusted not to let the surgery premises be razed to the ground. She had a habit of making bonfires in the garden to burn rubbish, but this habit extended to leaving the fires unattended. This was a constant cause of friction with the neighbours who lived in Chadwick Road as one of her eccentricities was to leave bottles and pressurised-cans in the rubbish. These objects when they exploded, deposited themselves in the neighbours' gardens, not to their delight, but to their distress and anger. Interestingly, the neighbours never once complained to any of the doctors of the housekeeper's behaviour, only to Ella herself. We did not find out about her *burning habits* until we nearly had our premises burnt down.

It was Saturday morning, Lynn and Jean, the two receptionists who were on duty that morning, had arrived at 8.45 am to prepare for the morning surgery. Consultations began at nine, medical cards had to be arranged in appointment order, the post had to be opened, and cards which it had not been possible to file on the previous day replaced in the filing cabinets. They opened the reception door hatch – which incidentally gives a view of the whole garden – and had the shock of their lives.

At the bottom of the garden the large sycamore tree was burning fiercely, so too was the garden shed which was sending sheets of flame into the neighbouring gardens. The wooden fence separating us from our neighbour at 107 was in flames, and as these premises at the time were unoccupied, no one had come to the surgery to warn and complain. What worried Lynn, the flames shooting across to our wooden surgeries situated in the garden might cause them to burst into flame any minute. She quickly telephoned the fire brigade, then went down herself with buckets of water to throw over our surgeries to prevent them from catching fire. Jean, on seeing the fire had become hysterical and was of no help. Her collapse was partnered by that of Ella who when she saw the conflagration after she returned from the corner shop with her bottle of milk promptly went into a faint.

Lynn's prompt action saved our surgeries, but we lost the garden shed, some fences, and the large sycamore tree which gave us shelter from the sun in the summer, and rain in the winter. We also lost for a time a much more important asset – this thank God has now been restored – the good will of our neighbours. We also learned why the garden shed had made such a good bonfire, Ella had used it as a storeroom for the jumble which she collected for the 5 club.

The 5 club, founded by Dr Cook, which met in the social service premises in Kirkwood Road, served to care for the needs of the lonely and mentally sick and held jumble sales to provide funds for the provision of amenities. As these sales only took place once or twice a year we had no objection to the club storing some of the articles for sale for a week or two before the day of the sale. What we had not bargained for was the use of our premises for longer periods, also the places used for the storage.

After our faithful housekeeper had left our employ, we found the shed was not the only place where Ella had stored jumble. Ted, who cleared out her upstairs bedrooms, found in them some sacks of jumble destined for the sale. On the day of the sale he collected the jumble, but he had not bargained for the fact our housekeeper was more eccentric than even he had thought possible. When he delivered the sacks to the church hall where the jumble sale was being held he was asked to open them and deposit the contents on the tables which had been specially prepared for their reception. A look of horror appeared on the faces of the onlookers when they saw what goodies Ted had taken the trouble to collect.

Two of the sacks did contain saleable items. The third sack however contained cats' mess, old bones from corsets, half a dirty vest, several pairs of knickers which had never seen soap in their lifetime and other such items which shall remain a secret.

As some wag remarked after the initial shock,
'we could have made a lot of money if we could
have sold the smell.'

It was intoxicating!

9

Infectious Diseases

A small, pasty-looking girl, Debbie, aged four years, was brought in to see me in January 1955 with no more than a snuffly cold and a bit of a cough. Her mother was so apologetic for bringing her in that I became embarrassed at the number of times she repeated her apologies. The family had been registered with me almost from the first day I arrived in Peckham and had never given me any problems. They had been model patients.

When mom therefore arrived with the girl who only had minimal symptoms I knew this child had to be really ill. Debbie had apparently been ill for four days with what appeared to be a bad cold, but although mother had kept her home from school and plied her with the usual cold remedies her condition had shown no signs of improvement. She had a bit of a temperature and a stiff neck, but after all, it was winter. Most of the girls in school had been away with similar symptoms and returned fit and well and mom could not understand why Debbie still complained of feeling 'under the weather'. Mom had only brought her in because the girl appeared too weak to stand on her own. She had actually been forced to carry the girl into the surgery. I had the shock of my life when she stood Debbie down on the floor of the consulting room, the child collapsed.

I examined this young lady from head to foot and apart from a red sore throat there was only one major sign – she had a paralysed left leg. My diagnosis was unequivocal, I had even in my limited experience already seen a few cases. Debbie had *poliomyelitis*. I sent her into hospital immediately and happily she recovered completely. The lesson this case taught me, never ever doubt a mother's concern about her child: she always knows best! I am happy to relate I have not seen another case in over forty years!

I saw many cases of *scarlet fever* in my early years but it had already lost its serious complications: the introduction of penicillin in most cases had aborted the heart and kidney complications. This disease had been taught to us thoroughly as students, but as with so many of the infectious diseases most of the difficulties had been unavoidable; we did not have the antibiotics to treat them.

I still remember the progress of scarlet fever as taught in medical school in 1945. On the first day, sore throat and high temperature. On the second day, rash and strawberry tongue. On the fourth day, raspberry tongue. Sixth to eighth day, the skin peels. I used to worry whether I would be able to differentiate a raspberry from a strawberry tongue, and whether I would be able to remember which came first. Fifty years have passed, I still see the disease, many cases of sore throats are probably mild cases as they are caused by the same organism, but the sight of a raspberry or strawberry tongue is somewhat exceptional. I saw one case in May 1994, this was the first for many years, and this child was even brought into the surgery! Parents now will bring their children into the surgery to be seen rather than insisting on a visit, something which would have been unthinkable when I started in practice.

For some unknown reason, in the early fifties, I saw many cases of *Bornholm disease*, but not having the convenience of a laboratory on tap I was not able to confirm the diagnosis by complement fixation tests. Bornholm disease, is due to the Coxsackie B virus, and as the symptoms mimic those of pleurisy due to other agents it is a difficult condition to diagnose just by physical examination. This disease caused me many anxious days and sleepless nights!

I was called out one day in 1962 to a young fellow in Chadwick Road, who was lying in bed in a pool of sweat. His sweating was not the cause of the call out, he had other symptoms too. He complained of itching, constipation, pains in the stomach and a shocking headache. It was not even these symptoms which were the reason he had called me out to visit him, it was for me to give him a certificate to give to his employers explaining his abscnce from work. Even the most inexperienced doctor would have been surprised when presented with this situation and I looked at him in astonishment when this request was made. The answer was only made apparent after I had examined him. I found that he had a tender enlarged liver and was jaundiced so I told him my diagnosis was catarrhal jaundice or infectious hepatitis. I continued to explain his condition in order as I thought to allay his anxiety – without giving him a chance to say a word. I advised him to stay in bed, rest, take plenty of fluids, avoid fats, and that I would revisit on the following day. To my consternation, ill as he was, as I was writing his certificate and certifying that he had infectious hepatitis, he stopped me in my tracks.

'I'm afraid you have the wrong diagnosis. I have spirochaetosis, I have had it before and it was exactly the same in my last attack,' he said.

I had never seen a case, have never seen one since, but luckily knew all about it. The disease *spirochaetosis icterohaemorrhagica* caused by the spirochaete leptospiro icterohaemorrhagica is a name not easily forgotten when one is a student. I also knew this disease was transmitted by the urine of infected rats – this chap was studying to be an accountant! I asked him why he was so certain of the diagnosis.

'Well, I have only just come back from a working holiday in Australia and caught it there,' he said.

'A funny way to spend a holiday working in the sewers,' was my reply.

'I have never been down a sewer in my life: I caught this while working in the paddy fields,' was his answer.

I had never realised until that moment that there were any paddy fields in Australia. He then explained, he had spent a year on a working holiday in Australia and one of the jobs had been in the paddy fields in the north. At that period it was not unusual for students to visit Australia and finance their stay there by working, it gave them the means of seeing the country. I understand that this method of seeing Australia is still used by our youngsters. Unfortunately, he was one of the unlucky ones who had been struck down with an unusual disease. He was however right in his diagnosis! I gave him a course of one of the sulphonamides at his insistence, but I believe he would have recovered anyway. He was back at his studies in six weeks.

Living conditions in small, terraced, over-populated, damp, drafty and insufficiently-heated houses, helped to spread diseases. We had outbreaks in the Peckham area in the fifties and sixties of *infectious hepatitis (catarrhal jaundice)*. I saw many cases which I treated at home and thankfully they all made a full recovery. They did however make for a heavy workload as there is no specific therapy and the patients could only be treated symptomatically. Treating the jaundiced patient who has a high temperature, especially if the jaundice persists for weeks, sometimes months, is not a pleasant occupation. The patient was usually a young adolescent, the parents were naturally very worried, and the diagnosis had to be made clinically. There was no biochemical backup available to general practitioners at that time and to get a night's sleep I occasionally had to beg the fever hospital at Hither Green to admit a patient. The reason for the hospital resistance was that we all knew the result would be the same if the patient remained at home.

Most of my problems in the early years were caused by the fact a doctor did not have the plethora of antibiotics available today. Repeat visits to an ill patient with an infection was therefore essential to make sure the treatment given was working. I could not always rely on sulphonamides (M & B), so in the severe cases I gave penicillin injections every four hours; in the less severe twice daily. My problem in Peckham was, as so few of my patients had telephones it was much safer for me to visit than to rely on them being able to reach me in an emergency. Visiting twice daily on a regular basis present general practitioners would find incomprehensible and intolerable, with modern medicines I do not blame them.

Chicken pox (varicella) was, and can still be a nasty, irritating, scabby disease with many complicating factors. I had the added difficulty in my diagnosis in differentiating it from *smallpox (variola)*. The textbook differentiation was, the skin lesions of chicken pox were first seen on the body, then spread to the face and scalp, finally the limbs. The stages were also important: macules, papules, vesicles and pustules. You could often find the pocks in the mouth and the pustules were not umbilicated.

Smallpox commenced in the extremities, did not follow the stages of chicken pox and what was more important, the pocks almost never occurred in the mouth. These pocks were also umbilicated. A macular, papular, pustular rash proceeding in this staged textbook fashion would have been easy to diagnose.

What however was one to make of Heather Peters, in 1964, who had a papular, pustular, umbilicated rash on her extremities? There were no pustules in her mouth, and to add to my difficulty she was toxic with a high enough temperature to boil an egg. Her two brothers were just recovering from chickenpox which as everyone knows is a highly infectious disease: this girl however was so ill I called in a consultant from Hither Green Hospital (an isolation hospital at that time) to see her for his opinion. Luckily we were both right – it was chickenpox. It is strange really, Miss Wood, the only patient whom I have ever seen who had a serious attack of smallpox had it mainly on her body. The telltale pock marks were still easily visible in 1987 from the attack she had suffered in the epidemic of 1918.

Immunisation against *diphtheria* and *pertussis* was already available at the time I entered practice. The problem with the pertussis (whooping cough) vaccine was it was thought to be the cause of convulsions and brain damage in some children. Many doctors were wary of giving it, indeed, my own three children were not given it for this very reason. The other main reason for not giving the whooping cough vaccine was that it did not always prevent an attack of whooping cough. As the diphtheria vaccine was almost one-hundred-per-cent successful it was reasoned that if a child had the combined vaccine and still caught whooping cough many parents would refuse to have their children vaccinated against diphtheria.

Vaccines against *rubella (german measles), hepatitis,*

measles, mumps, meningitis, rabies and polio were unknown. The massive trials in America to confirm the efficacy of Salk vaccine against poliomyelitis did not take place until 1954 and it was some years before it was in general use in this country. Before the vaccination of children against poliomyelitis became routine, it is obvious that every child with a bad cold was a suspected case and added to the GPs' work load.

Any patient who was at risk from *tetanus* (lockjaw), from being injured by a dirty object in the garden or from an animal bite was given an injection of tetanus antitoxin. One had to weigh up the risks as to whether it was better to risk the patient's life by giving an injection of antitoxin – this carried a risk of anaphylactic shock and sudden death – or just clean up the wound, pray and hope that he or she did not get tetanus. After all tetanus, even though it carried an almost one-hundred-per-cent mortality was a rare disease and only a few cases were reported yearly. One was always wary of giving antitoxin unless the situation demanded it. I had been a casualty officer, and an officer in the Royal Army Medical Corps before entering general practice and was therefore experienced in giving it – but always had adrenaline handy to counter any ill effects. Tetanus toxoid in those early years was still in its infancy and its efficacy not proved.

What was I to do in 1955, when my wife Louise, after pruning roses and scratching herself, suddenly developed a high temperature, felt unwell and began to complain of a stiff neck? I did not know what to do. I did not want to give her antitoxin then

271

have the pleasure of standing in the dock at the Old Bailey with the accusation of having murdered my wife! I rang my friend Dr Gordon in Colindale who had been my trainer in general practice in 1950, and sought his advice. He said go ahead and give antitoxin. I did. There were no complications.

Whooping cough was a nuisance in that it kept children away from school for weeks, sometimes months, and not having satisfactory antibiotics complicated the recovery. I still remember my hospital teaching from 1944 as to how to diagnose whooping cough. A child had to permutate two symptoms out of three.

1) Red-faced after a bout of coughing.
2) Whoop after a bout of coughing.
3) Vomit after a bout of coughing.

This teaching stood me in good stead when I was called out to see Brian Mason, in Chadwick Road, in February 1957. The time was three o'clock in the morning, not the best of times to make a differential diagnosis. Only one of the symptoms however mimicked whooping cough. He had a marked whoop, was quite ill, had difficulty in breathing, but no red face or vomitting.

My diagnosis was *laryngismus stridulus (croup)*, and my advice as to treatment was warm face flannels to the neck and ephedrine medicine. It worked! How different the treatment is today! The memory of this event reminds me how the attitude of a patient to a doctor has changed. I had told Mrs Mason I would revisit on the following day, after morning surgery, and duly found Brian in the morning completely recovered and lying in a bed with clean sheets. He had almost certainly jumped into bed on hearing my knock for from his appearance he must have been playing in the mud. He was not only indescribably filthy, he stank! I examined him, told mom that he could get up, and left. I knew there was going to be a reaction from Daisy Mason so after letting myself out of the front door silently stood behind it. I was not mistaken.

'Brian, you dirty-bugger, get out of the clean sheets! The doctor's gone. I am going to put them away.'

How differently the profession is treated today.

Rheumatic Fever, now rare in this country, was still prevalent. The treatment was to give massive doses of aspirin until the patient's ears buzzed and deafness possibly ensued. I remember quite vividly treating one of my patients before I had some experience of general practice on this regime and stepping up the doses of aspirin until she could no more tolerate the sickness which it caused. She actually rebelled and refused to continue treatment. To my horror, when I went to see her on the following day I found the poor girl had gone deaf. My worry however disappeared overnight. When I went back the next day, as she had stopped taking aspirin, the deafness had just as suddenly disappeared.

Ellen, now forty-five years old, had rheumatic fever in 1966. As her parents had refused to allow her to be admitted to hospital I treated her at home with aspirin and penicillin. I had now been in practice fourteen years. I no longer worried about the side effects of my treatment: all my patients made a complete recovery and like many of my colleagues I believed that no one was able to cure a patient as well as I could.

Ellen, had a high temperature, swollen flitting joints, and was so ill, in spite of my conceit she still gave me cause for concern. For the first three weeks of her illness I visited her twice a day and I was worried at the time that her heart might be affected. Thank heavens this did not occur and I still see her, a mother of three children, a grandmother, with no residual problems from her illness.

She had been, prior to her attack, a vivacious, ginger-haired, seventeen year old, but had rapidly become pale, wan and emaciated. After visiting her twice daily for several weeks it was only natural that I got to know this young lady very well. Even when I reduced my visitation to once daily I could not say that she was still not extremely ill. And it took another four weeks before I thought it wise to reduce my visits to three times weekly. I continued this regime for a further eighteen weeks and her face must have been by this time firmly imprinted in my memory. It was only then I thought it prudent to allow this pale, wan, strip of a girl, to get out of her bed and become ambulant. As I have already hinted, one would assume seeing her so often would have impressed her features indelibly on my mind. Not so!

A bright-eyed, beautifully made-up, well-groomed, young lady, bounced into my consulting room three weeks after I had given her permission to leave her home and I did not recognise her. I had spent a gruelling morning in the surgery with a succession of complaining patients whom I had to get off my back by referring to consultants in whom they had no faith. They were not only dissatisfied with me as a doctor but with the whole medical profession. They had also passed opinions on my treatment and the quality of training in our medical schools! Frustration was the password of that morning!

I looked at this girl standing in front of me. Although I knew I had definitely seen this young lady previously, for the life of me I could not remember where. The girl just looked at me without saying anything. The medical notes in my hand told me nothing of the history of this girl as the receptionist had provided me with the notes of another patient who had the same name and in the same age range. As I looked at the girl I was certain I had seen the face before, but where? My tired, chewed-up brain was in overdrive trying to place the face.

The girl as I have previously remarked had been when well a bundle of fun, a vivacious kid. She was now back to her usual self. In a flash she must have noticed bewilderment in my eyes, that I had not immediately recognised her. This was her chance to have some fun and embarrass me. She sat down for a few seconds, stood up, and while standing, slowly disrobed. She took off her coat, looked at me, smiled, then slowly took off her dress. She smiled, and before my startled eyes, slowly and carefully removed her brassiere. She now slowly sat down before me, *topless*. Neither of us had said a word whilst this disrobing was taking place. I had just sat motionless in my chair. I was not going to disturb her, to spoil a sight worth looking at. As no word had passed from either of us since she had entered my consulting room, I had now been put in the position of being lost for words! I just did not know what to say. With a twinkle in her eyes she now opened the conversation.

'You particularly asked me to come and see you today as you wanted to listen to my heart. I suppose you only recognise me by my body! I am a good girl, I have done as you asked and have stripped to save you time.'

It was then that I recognised her. By her voice of course!

Mumps was, and can still be a nasty complaint, especially if it is accompanied by complications. It is a disease which can cause the face to change its shape from an olive to a pumpkin, a patient with an oval elongated face changes beyond recognition. The old-fashioned remedy of providing warmth to the affected area of the face certainly did more harm than good, if only by the materials used. A smelly sock was one remedy. My grandmother's treatment of my mumps with a scarf dipped in urine is a remedy which I will never forget. *I can still smell having mumps!*

In mumps, the parotid glands at the sides of the face swell, and become painful and tender. The submandibular glands under the chin may become affected too giving the face the appearance of a full moon. In male adults, the pancreas and testicles may become involved giving rise to bellyache and discomfort in these organs. I have seen a scrotum the size of a football; in my experience, orchitis as a complication of mumps has not been all that unusual.

At an evening surgery in November 1964, my receptionist received a telephone call from a West Indian lady for Dr Crown, to visit her husband who was suffering from mumps. She was not worried over the diagnosis, her husband definitely had mumps, but Dr Crown had to visit her husband the same evening even if it was after the evening surgery. My receptionist thought the request was unreasonable as Dr Kwasny – who was my partner at the time – had already visited the husband that morning. It seemed pointless to her to ask me to visit again the same day.

Adonijah Smith, the patient, a lovely fellow, with a perpetual smile on his face, had registered with me on the day he had arrived in this country from Jamaica in 1955, and we had immediately established a rapport. My one and only receptionist was however having a hard time in trying to persuade Mrs Smith that a visit at that time of the night when he had already been seen that day and the diagnosis established was unnecessary. In desperation, the receptionist asked me to speak to Mrs Smith, and to prevent my receptionist from putting on her coat and walking out on me I did as she asked and went to the telephone.

I knew that Mrs O'Brien my receptionist at the time would be monitoring my reply, so before Mrs Smith could say one word I asked her to put me through to her husband. The poor woman hearing the sharp tone in my voice did as she was asked, and now, without even giving the patient a chance to open his mouth, I told Adonijah that I felt a visit that night was unnecessary. He had already been examined by a doctor that day and the diagnosis was not in doubt. I told him that I was in no mood to compromise. I had been disturbed in the middle of a busy surgery, in the middle of an examination, and my concentration had already been affected. What was all the fuss about? His reply, said without any emotion, succint, to the point, floored me.

'You are my doctor, Dr Crown. My balls are swollen up like footballs. I am dying! You are the only person who can do anything for me. If I die tonight, it won't be my fault!'

I had no answer. I promised to call to save his life. He is still a patient of mine.

Encephalitis is another complication of mumps which in my practice appeared in epidemic form. In 1957 there was a local outbreak, I saw five in my practice including my own son, Barry. It is strange really, encephalitis is reputed to be a rare complication, perhaps it was just the Peckham strain of Bellenden Road School. All the cases I attended went to this school. Two of the patients, girls, were in my son's class and were the first to go down with encephalitis and I sent them into hospital. When my son went down with the same symptoms I was loathe to send him into hospital so I asked a consultant to visit him at my home and decide whether hospitalisation would be necessary. The consultant from Great Ormond Street Children's Hospital came to see him and his advice was, as there was no treatment for this condition except aspirin and nursing care to leave the boy at home. The two children who suffered from encephalitis after my son I therefore kept at home too and treated in this fashion. All my patients – thank heavens – recovered completely although at the time they appeared to be desperately ill and gave me many sleepless, worrying nights.

Leprosy, is not a disease which one expects to see in Peckham, but I had the fortune, or perhaps I should say misfortune, of actually having a patient with this complaint, in 1964. A fifty-year-old Trinidadian, came to see me complaining of weakness in his right forearm and some vague tenderness in his elbow. The weakness had been present for some months, he had been hoping it would get better on its own, instead, the condition had been getting worse. He was a most uncomplaining fellow, a lovely chap, but as the problems were in his right elbow and arm and he was right-handed, the difficulty for him to work efficiently was obvious. I had diagnosed tennis elbow and treated him with creams, tablets and physiotherapy, all to no avail. I then sent him to see the orthopaedic consultant at the local hospital who prescribed various courses of physiotherapy. This had as much success as I had had with my treatment. I therefore referred him to another orthopaedic consultant at a different hospital for his opinion. This chap too prescribed various courses of physiotherapy: treatment here too was unsuccessful and made no impression on the weakness of his right arm. When one examined the fellow there was very little muscle wasting and consultants' opinions were 'neuropathy of unknown cause'.

This patient's good fortune was, he turned up one evening to my surgery where he was seen by Dr Prasad, a locum, who was taking the place of my partner who was on holiday. Dr Prasad was working in my partner's surgery upstairs, and he came down to tell me with a look of gratitude that I actually had a patient in my practice with leprosy. His pleasure on the find was due to the fact that although he claimed to have seen patients from most of the Far East with this complaint it was the first case he had seen of a man from the West Indies. I looked at Dr Prasad with such disbelief that he asked me to go upstairs with him. There was my Trinidadian, with his usual beaming smile, sitting quite happily in the chair and stripped to the waist. Dr Prasad now demonstrated to me the thickening of the chap's ulnar nerve at his right elbow and proceeded to give me a lecture on leprosy. I was shocked. This diagnosis had not even crossed my mind. I had never previously encountered a case of leprosy. Dr Prasad was certain of his diagnosis as he had at one time served as medical officer in charge of leper colonies in North West India. But as he could see that such a fancy diagnosis in Peckham was not one which lent itself easily to my doubting mind he referred him to the Hospital for Tropical Diseases for confirmation. The hospital in its reply wrote a letter of commendation to him for making such a brilliant clinical diagnosis. This is the only case of leprosy which I have ever seen in over forty years as a GP.

One thing I learned very quickly in my early years, the proverb *'empty vessels make the most noise'* applied to many of my patients. The child who screamed incessantly and who plagued the lives both of its mother and of its doctor was not the one who was dangerously ill. I have always been aware of the lethargic and uncomplaining child ever since I was called out one night to a child in Azenby Road in 1955. This house in Azenby Road no longer exists, it was demolished with a number of other houses to make way for what is now a recreation ground – Warwick Gardens.

In 1955, it was possible to drive from Lyndhurst Way through Azenby Road to Lyndhurst Grove. There were houses on each side of the road and there was a wide concrete area separating the two sides. This concreted area was said to be over a plague pit where some of the victims of the Great Plague of London (1664-5) were buried.

The visit to Azenby Road was to a young boy who would not stop screaming and who on examination I found to have an ear infection. His four-year-old sister was lying on her bed in the same room, uncomplaining. She was not asleep, her eyes were open, she was breathing rapidly and shallowly and coughing quietly. I was not asked to examine the girl, but providence has always been kind to me and prodded me to question mom about her.

Mary had always been a good girl, mom said. She had been a bit lethargic, had not wanted to play that day and as she had not wanted her supper had gone to bed early. She had always been a quiet girl so mom had not paid much attention. I looked at

Mary closely. Even in the darkened room it was obvious to me from the way she was breathing this child was desperately ill. This poor girl had been much too ill to have the strength to complain. She made no fuss at all when I removed the bedclothes to examine her. She just lay still. To mother's anguish and astonishment I told her little Mary had pneumonia and had to be admitted to hospital as an emergency for treatment.

This young patient, so early in my career, taught me a lot!